Enid Blyton's
Secret Seven
Annual

Well done, Secret Seven

KU-427-322

Purnell

PETER

Peter is Janet's brother and the leader of the Secret Seven. The Seven meet in a shed in Peter and Janet's garden, and Peter makes sure they abide by the rules of the society, using the correct password and wearing their special badges. Peter is quick-witted and spirited, and is looked up to by the other members of the Seven.

JANET

Janet is Peter's sister, and together they invented the Secret Seven. Janet is at school with Pam and Barbara, and is the most resourceful and independent of the three girls. Unlike some brothers and sisters, she and Peter get on well, and work happily together in the Seven!

GEORGE

George is at school with Colin, Peter and Jack. He and Colin often work together on the Seven's tasks. He is a helpful member of the Seven, but not a natural leader.

Contents

£1.75
In UK only

SBN 361 04565 4
Copyright © 1979 Darrell Waters Limited
"Well Done, Secret Seven" first published by Brockhampton
Press Ltd. (now Hodder and Stoughton Children's Books) in
1951
Published 1979 by Purnell Books, Berkshire House, Queen
Street, Maidenhead, Berkshire
Made and printed in Great Britain by Purnell and Sons
Limited, Paulton (Bristol) and London

RBARA

ara is at school with Janet and
. She is a sensible and reliable
ber of the Seven, but is a little
timid and cautious than the
two girls.

JACK

Jack is brave and energetic and is
really second in command of the
Seven after Peter. He usually
accompanies Peter on the more
difficult and dangerous of the Secret
Seven's adventures. He has a mischievous sister called Susie, who is
not a member of the Seven, and who
is always trying to ruin their plans!

COLIN

Colin is a schoolfriend of Peter,
George and Jack. He and George
often work as a pair on the Secret
Seven's adventures. He is quieter
than Peter or Jack, and usually
follows their instructions.

PAM

Pam is a schoolfriend of Janet and
Barbara. She is quite adventurous,
but can be a little quarrelsome and
stubborn sometimes! Peter keeps
her in line, though!

Introduction

Here's the second *Secret Seven Annual* for you to enjoy!

The mixture is as before, with the whole of the exciting title story—'Well Done, Secret Seven'—in text and picture strip. Added to this, there are all sorts of features, projects, quizzes and puzzles, all linked in some way with the title story.

Animal lovers will find lots to interest them here—an article on kitten care, facts about squirrels, and an article on spaniels, inspired by Scamper! There's a fascinating account of Britain's waterways, and young cooks will find a scrumptious recipe to try. Those of you who like growing things can discover how to make your own beautiful miniature garden. All this and more, together with brain-teasers, games and puzzles! There's something for everyone to enjoy!

Look out for the next *Secret Seven Annual,* and its companion for readers of between nine and twelve years old, the *Famous Five Annual.*

Chapter 1

The Secret Seven Meet

'WHERE'S my badge? Where's my badge?' said Janet. 'I know I put it into this drawer.' And out of the drawer came handkerchiefs, socks, and ribbons, flying in the air.

'Janet!' said Mummy, crossly. 'Do look what you are doing—I only tidied that drawer this morning. What is it you want—your Secret Seven Badge?'

'Yes! There's a meeting this morning, and I can't go without my badge,' said Janet. 'Peter wouldn't let me into the shed, I know he wouldn't. He's awfully strict about badges.' And away went another shower of handkerchiefs into the air.

'Well, you certainly won't find it in the drawer now,' said Mummy, and she bent and picked up a little round badge with the letters 'S.S.' worked neatly on it. 'You have thrown it out of the drawer with your hankies, silly!'

'Oh give it to me, Mummy, give it to me!' cried Janet. But Mummy wouldn't.

'No. You pick up all those things first and tidy them in the drawer,' she said.

'But the Secret Seven meet in five minutes!' cried Janet. 'Peter's down in our shed already.'

'Then you can be late,' said Mummy, and walked out of the room with the little badge! Janet groaned. She picked up everything and stuffed it back into the drawer as tidily as she could in a hurry. Then she tore downstairs.

'I've done it, Mummy, and I *promise* I'll do it better when the meeting is over.'

Mummy laughed. She held out the

little badge to Janet. 'Here you are. You and your Secret Seven meetings! How you can bear to meet in that stuffy little shed this hot weather I don't know! *Must* you keep the door *and* the window shut all the time?'

'We have to,' said Janet, pinning on the badge proudly. 'It's a *very* Secret Society, and we can't have anyone listening to our meetings. Not that much has happened lately. We really need something to liven us up—an adventure like the last one.'

'Take the biscuit-tin down with you,' said Mummy. 'And you can have a bottle of orangeade. Here's Scamper come to find you!'

The lovely golden spaniel came trotting into the room. 'Woof,' he said to Janet. 'Woof!'

She went down the garden-path, hugging the biscuit-tin and the bottle of orangeade

'Yes, yes—I know I'm late,' said Janet, giving him a pat. 'I suppose Peter sent you to fetch me. Come along. Thanks for the biscuits and orangeade, Mummy.'

She went down the garden-path, hugging the biscuit-tin and the bottle of orangeade. As she came near the shed, she heard voices. It sounded as if all the other six were there!

Janet banged on the door, and Scamper flung himself against it too.

'Password!' yelled six voices.

'Adventure!' yelled back Janet, giving the password for that week. No one could go to a meeting without saying the password.

The door flew open, and Peter, Janet's brother, stood there, frowning. 'Any need to yell out the password like that?' he said.

'Sorry,' said Janet. 'You all yelled out at me, and I just yelled back. Anyway, there's no one to hear. Look, I've brought the biscuit-tin and some orangeade.'

Peter looked to see if she had on her badge. He had seen his sister hunting madly for it ten minutes back, and he had made up his mind he wouldn't allow her in if she hadn't found it. But there it was, pinned to her dress.

Janet went into the shed. Peter shut the door and bolted it. The window was shut too. The hot summer sun streamed in at the one window, and Janet blew out her cheeks.

'My goodness—it's boiling hot in here! Honestly, I shall melt.'

'We're *all* melting,' said Pam. 'I think this is a silly place to have our weekly meetings when it's so hot. Why can't we

'I've got a couple of cushions up there,
and a box to keep things in'

have them out in the woods somewhere, in the shade of a tree?'

'No,' said Jack at once. 'My sister Susie would always be hanging around —we wouldn't be a Secret Society any more.'

'Well, couldn't we think of somewhere cool and hidden, where nobody would find us?' said Colin. 'For instance, I've got a hiding-place in my garden where nobody can find me at all, and it's as cool and as hidden as can be.'

'Where is it?' asked Jack.

'Up a tree,' said Colin. 'We've a big tree with some broad branches half-way up, and I've got a couple of cushions up there, and a box to keep things in. It's cool and breezy, and the branches swing about in the wind. And I've got a jolly good view all round too. I can always see if anyone is coming!'

They all listened to this speech in silence. Then they looked at one another, their eyes shining.

'Marvellous idea!' Peter said. 'We'll do it ourselves! A house up a tree where we could meet and nobody know! We'll do it!'

Chapter 2

A Wonderful Idea

IT'S FINE. THERE ARE ABOUT SIX BRANCHES HERE, ALL ON THE SAME LEVEL, MORE OR LESS, AND THERE'S A HOLE IN THE TRUNK TOO. IT WOULD MAKE A FINE CUPBOARD. COME ON UP! THERE'S ROOM FOR EVERYONE!

ONE BY ONE THE OTHERS CLIMBED UP AND JOINED JACK...

THIS IS EASY-SOME PARTS OF THIS TRUNK SEEM AS THOUGH THEY WERE MADE FOR FOOT-HOLDS.

IT'S THE BIGGEST TREE IN THE WOOD, I SHOULD THINK. WHAT LUCK TO HAVE SO MANY BROAD BRANCHES ALL ABOUT THE SAME LEVEL. WHERE'S THE HOLE YOU TOLD US ABOUT, JACK?

HERE. IT GOES DOWN ABOUT TWO FEET.

SEE? IT WOULD MAKE A FINE STORE FOR US—JUST WHAT WE WANT. WELL, SHALL WE MAKE THIS OUR SECRET SEVEN TREE, OUR NEW MEETING-PLACE?

OH, YES!

PETER TOOK OUT HIS NOTEBOOK AND PENCIL...

RIGHT, SUGGESTIONS AND IDEAS ONE AT A TIME, PLEASE. I'LL WRITE THEM ALL DOWN.

Tree ~ house Cookies

There's nothing like some crunchy cookies to keep you going when you have a mystery to solve, as the Secret Seven well know! But there's no mystery about their favourite 'Tree-house Cookies'—they are simple to make and scrumptious to eat. Peter and Janet sometimes make them for the Seven to munch during their secret meetings, and here they share with *you* the recipe for cooking up these tasty treats!

(Do be careful when handling the hot saucepan and baking tray, and be sure to ask a grown-up to stand by in case you need a hand.)

You will need
2 oz (55 g) plain flour
2 oz (55 g) porridge oats
2 oz (55 g) brown sugar
2 oz (55 g) butter or margarine
1 tablespoon golden syrup
$\frac{1}{2}$ level teaspoon bicarbonate of soda
(Sufficient for 12 to 15 cookies)
kitchen scales
small saucepan
wooden spoon
kitchen knife
tablespoon and teaspoon
baking tray
oven-gloves

For a *special* Secret Seven treat, pipe some icing on to the cookies in the shape of the secret 'SS' sign. Delicious!

1. Set oven at 325°F on electric cooker or mark 4 on gas cooker. Put the butter (or margarine) and syrup into a saucepan and warm on a cooker ring. Using a wooden spoon, blend together until melted.

2. Take the saucepan off the ring (remember to turn it off) and, with a wooden spoon, stir in the porridge oats, brown sugar, flour and bicarbonate of soda. Mix thoroughly.

3. Grease the baking tray, that is, rub a knob of margarine (or cooking lard) all over the surface of the tray. (This is to prevent the cookies sticking to the tray when in the oven.)

4. Take a small amount of the mixture and roll it into a ball in the palms of your hands. Place the ball on the tray and press down on it to slightly flatten it. Repeat until you have used all the mixture, allowing about 5 cm space between each ball.

5. When the oven has reached the required heat, place the tray on the top shelf. Cook for 15 to 20 minutes until golden brown. Wearing oven-gloves, take the tray from the oven (remember to turn it off). Leave the cookies to cool before removing them from the tray.

6. When they are cold, pop them into a tin or polythene container to keep them fresh. Now your tasty tree-house cookies are ready for that secret meeting, or for whenever you fancy a crunchy snack!

Chapter 3

The Big Tree

EVERYONE was full of ideas. 'We could bring some small boards to put across the branches and make a proper little platform,' said Colin. 'We've got some in our shed at home.'

'And rope to tie them on with,' said Jack.

'Yes, and cushions to sit on,' said Pam. 'Only we'd have to stuff them in the hole in the tree whenever we left, in case it rained.'

'Can't do that. The hole's not big enough,' said Jack.

'Well, I could bring an old waterproof sheet—a rubber one—to cover up any of our things when we leave,' said Barbara. 'Then they would be quite all right.'

'Good idea,' said Peter, scribbling fast in his note-book. 'Any more ideas?'

'Stores for the cubby-hole in the tree,' said Janet. 'Unbreakable mugs and things like that. I'll bring those. Mummy always lets us have them when we want them, so long as we take them back sometime.'

'This is fine,' said Peter, scribbling quickly. 'Boards to make a platform. You can bring those, Colin.'

'Rope to tie them with,' said Jack. 'I'll bring that.'

'Cushions for me,' said Pam.

'Rubber sheet for me,' said Barbara.

'Mugs for me,' said Janet. 'What about you, George?'

'I'll bring some food for the cubby-hole,' said George.

'Smashing!' said Peter. 'And I'll bring

'Don't you go and tell that awful sister of yours, Jack'

the drinks. Golly, we're going to have a glorious time. It will be a wonderful meeting-place. Don't you go and tell that awful sister of yours, Jack.'

'As if I'd tell Susie!' said Jack, indignantly. 'When shall we begin to make the tree-house?'

'Why not tomorrow?' said Peter. 'Nobody is going away to the sea just yet. It shouldn't take us long to put everything together up here. This place is just *made* for a tree-house!'

A loud and mournful howl rose up from the foot of the tree. Then there came a scrabbling noise.

'Oh, poor Scamper!' said Janet. 'He's been as good as anything waiting for us. I guess he wishes he could climb like our cat. He'd be up beside us in half a jiffy!'

'We're coming, Scamper,' called Peter. He took one last look round the tree. 'It really couldn't be better,' he said. 'And

'Good idea,' said Peter, scribbling fast in his note-book

there's only one more thing to hope for.'

'What's that?' asked Jack, beginning to climb down.

'Something for the Secret Seven to *do*,' said Peter. 'We haven't had any adventure or mystery or excitement for ages.'

'I'm glad you said that,' said Pam. 'When you say things never happen— they always do!'

'I hope you're right,' said Peter. He parted the leaves of the tree behind him. 'What a long way we can see!' he said. 'Right over the wood, and across to the hill. I can see the road winding up the hill too, and cars on it.'

He pointed to what looked almost like a small cave in a nearby tree

'Come on,' called Jack, who was half-way down the tree now. 'It's getting jolly late. I shall get into a row, I know I shall. My mother says our meetings always last an hour too long!'

'Well, this was a jolly good one any-how,' said Colin, slithering down much too fast. 'Golly, now I've torn my shorts.'

'I should think so, going down the tree as if it was a slippery-slip!' said Barbara.

Scamper gave them a tremendous welcome. He leapt on one after another as the Secret Seven jumped down to the ground, barking and licking with all his might. Peter laughed.

'Poor old Scamper—you won't like our new meeting-place, will you? I say— look—what about giving Scamper that hole over there as a kind of kennel when we are up the tree?'

He pointed to what looked almost like a small cave in a nearby tree. It was old and rotten, and a hole had appeared at the foot of its trunk. It would just about fit Scamper.

'We could put one of his rugs in there, and a bone, so that he would know it was his place,' said Peter. 'And we could say, "On guard, Scamper!" to him, so that he would stay there till we came down.'

He wagged his tail and ran in front of them

'Oh *yes*—he would be our sentinel,' said George. 'He'd make an awfully good one. He would bark as soon as anyone came near.'

They all felt happy now that they had made a good plan for Scamper. He wouldn't be able to come up the tree and join their meetings as he did in the shed—but at least he would be doing *something* for them and feeling important because he was on guard.

'Woof,' said Scamper, exactly as if he understood every word, and agreed thoroughly. He wagged his tail and ran in front of them. *He* knew it was dinner-time, if they didn't!

19

Do you wonder what sort of tree the Seven chose to make their tree-house in? Well, they are keeping it a secret, for they say there aren't many trees of that type in Windy Woods, and if they revealed what type of tree it is, Jack's mischievous sister Susie might try to find it so she could listen in to the Seven's secret meetings. But would you recognise it even if you knew what it was called? To help you identify some of the trees found growing in this country, the Seven have each chosen one of their favourite trees and here tell you a little about them. The pictures of the trees and their leaves will help you identify them, and then you may just guess what sort of tree that tree-house is in!

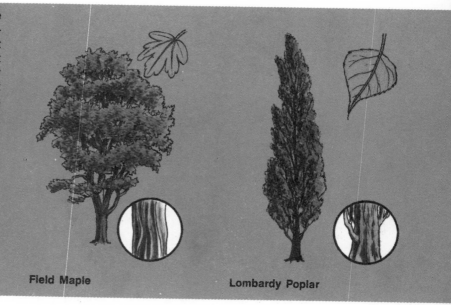

Field Maple   **Lombardy Poplar**

George's Choice
FIELD MAPLE

The Field Maple (also called the Common or Hedge Maple) is one of our smaller trees, growing to between 6 and 12 metres in height. It can be found along the wayside or in hedgerows, where it appears more like a bush than a tree. Its leaves are anything from 5 to 10 centimetres across and grow in pairs, always opposite each other. The young Field Maple's bark is pale brown with rough, deep cracks. As it grows older, though, it becomes much smoother.

Janet's Choice
SILVER BIRCH

The poet Coleridge called the Birch 'The Lady of the Woods', and it is certainly a very pretty and graceful tree. But its slenderness and beauty are misleading, for this is one of our hardiest trees. It grows happily in very hot and very cold conditions, provided it has plenty of light; it will not grow well in shade. Fully grown, it reaches about 14 metres, although it can climb to 24. It is easily recognised by its attractive silvery-white bark. Its leaves, which look glossy and leathery, are quite small, measuring little more than $2\frac{1}{2}$ centimetres at the widest part.

Jack's Choice
COMMON OAK

You can't mistake the Oak tree: its massive trunk (often 3 metres wide, but occasionally as much as 11 metres) and wide-spreading branches make it the largest of our native trees. In forests, where it has to compete with other trees, its branches are drawn up, giving the Oak a height of anything up to $39\frac{1}{2}$ metres. But in a more isolated setting the tree will grow no more than 18 metres, preferring to spread its limbs outwards. The Oak's bark is thick and rough and deeply furrowed. Its leaves, easily spotted by their familiar wavy-edged shape, grow to about $7\frac{1}{2}$ centimetres in length.

Pam's Choice
LOMBARDY POPLAR

The Lombardy Poplar, named after the region in Italy where it first appeared, is the only tree outside the coniferous (cone-bearing) family to send its branches straight upwards into a spire shape. This makes it very easy to spot, and it will be seen both in the country and the town, where Lombardy Poplars are often grown together to make an effective screen against wind and noise. Apart from its very

dignified appearance, this tree can also be identified by the deep, spiral furrows of its bark. At the base the bark is almost black, while higher up it is grey-brown.

Barbara's Choice
ASH

The Ash is a very striking tree—light and graceful, yet at the same time dominating. For this reason it has been called the 'Venus of the Woods'. Found in meadows, hedgerows and on the outskirts of woods, it is late in producing its leaves and early in losing them. There are as many as fifteen leaflets to one leaf, which may be anything up to 23 centimetres in length. Fully-grown, the Ash will reach between 24 and 30 metres. Its bark is pale grey and has rough, shallow furrows.

Peter's Choice
BEECH

The Beech is easily recognised by its huge, towering trunk, its smooth, grey bark, and its thick, rambling roots spread above the ground. It produces masses of oval, smooth-faced leaves (5 to $7\frac{1}{2}$ centimetres long) which provide shade on the hottest day. Because the

Secret Seven Tree Hunt

foliage is so dense, and because the Beech roots in the surface soil, little, if anything, grows in its shade. Look up and you'll probably see another of its distinctive features —the dividing of the trunk into several trunks, each the size of the main one.

Colin's Choice
HORSE CHESTNUT

The finest of all the flowering trees, the Horse Chestnut is often to be found in public parks and gardens. There, its commanding appearance and supply of 'conkers' make it a favourite with both nature-lovers and schoolboys. Curiously, it has nothing to do with chestnuts—the edible chestnut is produced by another tree—but the 'horse' part of its name is thought to be linked to the horseshoe-like mark left on the bark of young branches when a leaf has fallen.

The tree's leaves are one of its most striking features: normally there are seven leaflets (often mistaken for actual leaves) to one leaf, and this may be as much as $45\frac{1}{2}$ centimetres across. The Horse Chestnut grows to between 24 and 30 metres, and its bark, fairly smooth at the bottom, develops into rough scales.

Beech

Common Oak

Silver Birch

Horse Chestnut

Ash

Chapter 4

Making the Tree-house

THE next day was really very exciting. If anyone had been in Windy Woods he or she would have been most astonished to see the file of children going down the path, each carrying some kind of load.

They had all met at Peter's house with their goods. Janet, his sister, had mugs and plates and spoons. Colin had a set of boards, which Jack had to help him with. Jack had coiled yards and yards of rope round his waist and looked really most peculiar.

Barbara was carrying a big rubber sheet carefully folded, and she was helping Pam with a set of old cushions.

'They're a bit dirty and flattened out,' said Pam, 'but I didn't think that would matter. I got them out of the garden-shed, they've been there ages. I could only find six, so we'll have to get another somewhere.'

Janet ran to get one from her garden-shed, where the Secret Seven usually held their meetings. That made seven cushions, one for everyone.

George had some chocolate, and also a fine big tin of mixed biscuits. 'Mother gave me them,' he said. 'She says your mother keeps supplying our Society with food, and it's her turn now.'

'Jolly fine,' said Peter, with much approval. 'What a smashing tin!' He had taken some money from his money-box and had bought a bottle of lemonade and one of orangeade, and he also had two bottles full of water to use with the drinks.

Even Scamper had to carry something! He had one of his little rugs rolled up tightly and tied with string. He was carrying it in his mouth, feeling most important. He loved it when the children really let him take part in everything they were doing.

'Woooooof-woof,' he said, with his mouth full of rug.

'He says he likes to be carrying something like everyone else,' said Janet. 'That's right, isn't it, Scamper?'

Scamper wagged his tail, and almost

'Woooooof-woof,' he said, with his mouth full of rug

dropped his rug in his longing to bark properly. 'Ooooof,' he said.

The Seven set off down the path, came to Windy Woods, and made their way to their tree. 'We ought to carve "S.S." on the trunk, for Secret Seven,' said Pam.

'Well, we can't,' said Peter. 'My father says that scribbling on walls and pavements and carving on trees is only done by idiots. And if anyone in the Secret Seven wants to be an idiot he can jolly well get out.'

'I only said we *ought* to carve "S.S."' said Pam, quite hurt. 'I didn't mean that we should. You know I'm not an idiot.'

'Yes. I do know,' said Peter. 'I was only just telling you what my father said. Let's make Scamper his little "sentry-box" place before we go up the tree.'

It was fun showing Scamper his 'sentry-box'. He sniffed all round, and then sat down at the entrance, his mouth open as if he were smiling.

'He's pleased. He's smiling,' said Janet. 'Come out, Scamper, and we'll put your rug in. Then you'll know this is

your own place—your "sentry-box." And you're the sentinel on guard. ON GUARD, Scamper. You know what that means, don't you?'

'Woof,' said Scamper, and looked suddenly serious. He ran out.

Peter stuffed his rug into the hole. Then he dropped a bone there for Scamper, and then he put an old cap of his in the hole too.

'On guard, Scamper,' he said, pointing. 'On guard, old fellow. Very important. Guard my cap for me till I come back. On guard!'

Scamper went back into the hole, sniffed solemnly at the cap, then at the bone. He turned round and sat himself upright at the entrance to the hole again, looking important. Nothing would now make him leave his 'sentry-box' until Peter told him he might. He

was a very, very good guard when he knew he had to be.

'Now we can get on with our own job without old Scamper leaping round us and barking and getting in the way all the time,' said Peter. 'Let's tie the boards and the rubber sheet to the ropes—then one of us can go up the tree with the rope-end, and pull the whole lot up at once.'

This seemed a very good idea, but wasn't. Peter didn't tie the ropes securely enough round the boards—and as Jack was hauling the package up the tree, a rope slipped and down came all the boards and the rubber sheet, bumping and slipping against the tree!

One board hit Colin on the shoulder, and the rubber sheet unfolded and fell neatly over Pam's head. The others squealed with laughter as Pam yelled and struck out, wondering what had happened to her.

'Oh dear—sorry!' said Peter, pulling

the sheet off poor Pam. 'We'll tie the things more firmly this time.'

'You let *me* tie them,' said Colin, rubbing his shoulder. 'I'm not going to have a shower of heavy boards fall on me again!'

'This is *fun*,' said George. 'This is really *fun*! I bet nobody ever had such fun making a tree-house before!'

The rubber sheet unfolded and fell neatly over Pam's head

Chapter 5
Great Fun

THE SEVEN WERE REALLY ENJOYING THEMSELVES MAKING THE TREE-HOUSE – BUT OCCASIONALLY THERE WERE PROBLEMS!

OH DEAR, THERE GOES ANOTHER BOARD. WHOSE TURN IS IT TO CLIMB DOWN AFTER THAT ONE?

LOOK, WITH ALL OF US SITTING ABOUT ON THE BRANCHES THAT WE WANT TO PUT THE BOARDS ON IT'S REALLY DIFFICULT. YOU GIRLS GET DOWN TO THE GROUND.

OH, ALL RIGHT. COME ON.

BUT THAT DIDN'T STOP THINGS FALLING!

AT LAST THE JOB WAS DONE...

QUITE SAFE NOW. WE'VE DONE A JOLLY GOOD JOB. YOU CAN COME UP AGAIN NOW, GIRLS.

BLOW! THERE GOES ONE OF THE CUSHIONS! WELL, IT CAN WAIT. THERE'LL BE ANOTHER BOARD FALLING DOWN IN A MINUTE, AND WHO-EVER GETS THAT CAN GET THE CUSHION TOO.

THERE! OUR NEW HEADQUARTERS – MEETING-PLACE OF THE SECRET SEVEN SOCIETY. SENTINEL ON GUARD DOWN BELOW. EVERYTHING READY TO TACKLE OUR NEXT ADVENTURE, IF ONLY IT COMES!

I DON'T MIND IF IT DOESN'T. THIS IS ENOUGH ADVENTURE FOR ME. FANCY HAVING A TREE-HOUSE LIKE THIS! AH – HERE COMES THE WIND!

LOVELY! I FEEL AS IF I'M ON A SHIP NOW – THAT SWAYING FEELING IS JUST LIKE BEING IN A BOAT.

LOOK, IT'S HALF PAST TWELVE. LET'S HAVE A BISCUIT AND A DRINK, AND GO HOME. WE CAN COME BACK THIS AFTERNOON. WE'LL BRING BOOKS AND A GAME AND ENJOY OURSELVES.

BUT SCAMPER HAD OTHER IDEAS!

BUT SCAMPER WOULDN'T STOP LEAPING AND BARKING TILL THE BOY MOVED RIGHT AWAY FROM THE TREE...

I DON'T KNOW WHY YOU WON'T LET ME CLIMB THAT TREE, BUT IF YOU DON'T WANT ME TO, I WON'T. I CAN ALWAYS COME BACK WHEN YOU'RE NOT HERE, ANYWAY.

HE'S GONE—THANKS TO SCAMPER. BUT I WONDER IF HE WILL COME BACK...?

I DON'T THINK HE WILL. I THINK HE WAS JUST HAVING A WALK THROUGH THE WOODS— WITH HIS KITTEN! FUNNY THING, THOUGH, TO TAKE A KITTEN ABOUT WHEN YOU GO FOR A WALK.

WHAT'S THE MATTER? WHAT ARE YOU SO EXCITED ABOUT? GET DOWN. IF YOU'RE AFTER MY KITTEN YOU CAN THINK AGAIN. GET DOWN, I SAY!

LET'S FORGET ABOUT HIM AND HAVE A GAME OF CARDS. I PUT SOME IN HERE. AND WHAT ABOUT A DRINK? I'M AWFULLY THIRSTY.

JUST THEN THEIR ATTENTION WAS ATTRACTED BY ANOTHER VISITOR— THIS TIME A WELCOME ONE!

HALLO! HOW ARE YOU? AND HOW'S YOUR FAMILY?

YOU WON'T GO ROBBING OUR CUBBY-HOLE WHEN WE'RE NOT HERE, WILL YOU?

BUT THE CARD GAME WASN'T A SUCCESS — THE WIND KEPT BLOWING THE CARDS OFF THE PLATFORM!

BLOW! THERE GOES ANOTHER! I THINK DOMINOES WOULD BE BETTER. AT LEAST THEY WOULDN'T BLOW OFF SO EASILY.

THAT REMINDS ME— IT'S FIVE O'CLOCK — TIME WE WEREN'T HERE. COME ON, LET'S PACK UP.

ALL RIGHT. AND WE'LL TAKE SCAMPER A CHOCOLATE BISCUIT FOR BEING SUCH A GOOD GUARD!

A Dominoes Puzzle

'I'll bring some dominoes tomorrow,' said George, when he got fed up with the wind flipping the playing cards off the tree-house platform. But what sort of dominoes game do you suppose George had in mind? Although the Seven love playing dominoes in the normal way, they also enjoy the special dominoes puzzles which George sets for them. He uses two sets of bricks, laying them out in a sort of maze pattern. The idea is that by starting at the double blank in the top left-hand corner, you have to find your way along a route which eventually brings you back to the starting point. The only rule you have to follow is that you can move from one domino to another only if the touching halves bear the same number of pips. It sounds simple, but there are several dead-end routes built into the puzzle to trick you, so it may take longer than you think to find your way back to the beginning!

George has worked out the puzzle below specially for readers of this adventure, and he hopes you have lots of fun doing it. When you have completed it, and tried it out on your friends, why not make up your own dominoes puzzle? If you don't have two sets of bricks, cut out another set from cardboard and draw the pips on with a felt-tipped pen.

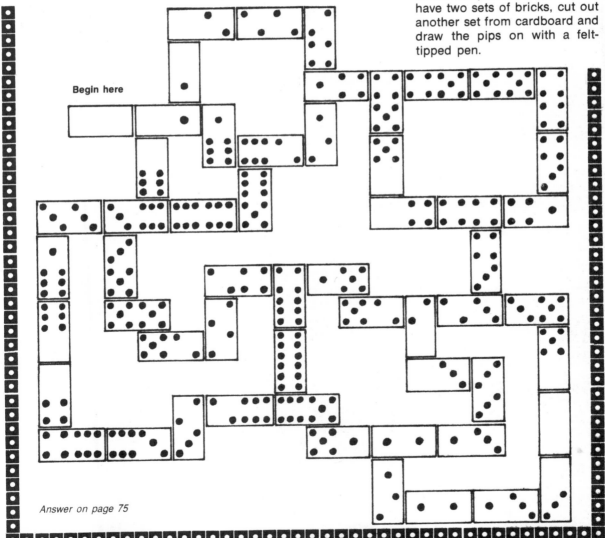

Begin here

Answer on page 75

All About Squirrels

Photographs by Frank W. Lane

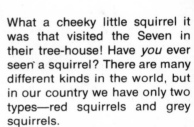

The grey squirrel is larger, bolder and more common than the red squirrel *(below)*

What a cheeky little squirrel it was that visited the Seven in their tree-house! Have *you* ever seen a squirrel? There are many different kinds in the world, but in our country we have only two types—red squirrels and grey squirrels.

The red squirrel is one of our most attractive wild animals, especially when sitting on its haunches, its little tufted ears erect and its feathery tail curled up behind its back. It weighs about 283 g and is around 38 cm long, including the tail.

But the grey squirrel, which is what the Seven saw, is both larger (weighing about 538 g and measuring 50 cm long) and more common. It is bolder than the red squirrel too. Whereas the red squirrel spends most of its time up in the trees of the pine forest, where it is most at home, the grey squirrel is often to be seen darting about on the floor of a wood, and even in some town gardens where there are lots of trees.

Although you cannot be sure of seeing a squirrel each time

Left: Young squirrels cling to the knotty bark of a tree

Above: The red squirrel is one of our prettiest wild animals

you walk through a wood, there are plenty of tell-tale signs that will help you to know where to look for them.

Look up in the trees and you may spot their nests, or 'dreys'. In the winter the drey is built of leafy twigs and lined with leaves, bark and moss or grass. It is dome-shaped and may be seen wedged in the angle between the trunk and a branch. This drey, which is built quite high in the tree, is also used as a nursery for the squirrel's kittens. Usually two litters of one to seven (but usually three) are born each year during March and June.

In summer the squirrel builds another drey, which usually is no more than a platform of twigs built out in a branch, and lower down than the winter drey.

Another sign that there's a squirrel about may be found on the ground. For a start, you may see its footprints (pictured opposite), but it is more likely that you will spot left-overs from its meals — remains of acorns, pine cones and nut shells—scattered around the foot of a tree or stump.

In the spring, other clues to the squirrel's presence may be young trees with their bark stripped off (the squirrel does this to get at the sap) or with new buds eaten away.

The squirrel's diet also includes soft fruits and berries in the summer and toadstools in the autumn.

Food is difficult to find during the winter, so the squirrel prepares for this by burying nuts and sometimes fungi in the earth. On winter days it ventures out of its drey, sniffing out the hidden food, and in this way keeping itself fed through to the spring.

If you wish to see a squirrel feeding you must go quietly through the woods, for at the slightest sound the squirrel will scurry up the nearest tree: the sound may signal danger from its most dangerous enemy, the pine marten. The marten can jump as far and as fast as its prey, and for the squirrel every chase through the trees is a matter of life or death.

The squirrel's other enemies include owls and eagles—and sometimes man, for this lovable little creature is far from loved by the forester, whose young trees can be ruined by the squirrel's habit of stripping saplings of their bark and buds.

Chapter 6

Next Morning

THE next morning they all met at Peter's house again and went off to Windy Woods. Some of them had things to eat, and Peter had the drinks again. Janet had a big book with her. She had promised to lend it to Colin for the day.

'Here's Daddy's book that I told you about,' she said. 'It's all about ships—every single ship there is. I told you I'd bring it to show you. But Daddy says I've GOT to give it back to him in two or three days' time. So don't keep it too long.'

'Thanks awfully,' said Colin, and took it, very pleased. He loved ships, and this was really a wonderful book. He knew he must be very careful with it indeed.

Scamper trotted with them, as usual. They came to Windy Woods and made their way to their tree. Scamper at once put himself into his 'sentry-box' and sat there, serious and important.

'Woof,' he said, and Janet patted him.

'Yes, we know you'll be on guard,' she said. 'Good dog!'

They all climbed up. Peter undid the rubber sheet from the cushions and spread them out over the platform. Just as he had finished the girls gave a startled cry. 'Look! The lid of the biscuit-tin is off, and most of the biscuits are gone! We left quite a lot, but only a few are here. And some of the chocolate we left is gone too, and the lemonade bottle is empty. It was half full.'

They all looked into the cubby-hole. Yes—the biscuits were certainly gone.

The Secret Seven looked at one another. Then Janet spoke suddenly.

'Do you know what I think? I think it's that cheeky little squirrel! I bet he came here after we had gone, looked into our cubby-hole, and took our things. Squirrels are very clever!'

'But what about the lemonade?' asked Peter, doubtfully.

'Squirrels use their paws like monkeys,' said Janet. 'We've seen them holding nuts in their paws and chewing them. I'm sure that squirrel would be clever enough to take the cork out of the bottle. I expect it emptied some of the lemonade out. It wouldn't like the taste.'

'I can believe in a squirrel that takes a cork out of a bottle and even empties some of the lemonade out,' said Peter. 'But I can't somehow believe in a squirrel that puts the cork back again. I believe it's that boy!'

'So do I,' said George. But the others didn't. They were sure it was the squirrel.

'Anyway, don't let's worry,' said Jack. 'We've got plenty of food today. If the squirrel likes a few biscuits and a bit of chocolate, he can have them.'

They had been sensible that morning and had brought dominoes to play with. However, they could just as well have brought cards, because there was no wind. The sun was not to be seen, and the clouds were low.

'I hope it's not going to rain,' said Colin, looking up. 'I believe it is.'

The Secret Seven looked at one another

'Well, we shan't feel it much, hidden away in the middle of a thick old tree,' said Pam. 'I don't expect we'll get a single drop on our platform.'

When it did begin to rain, and the

'I'd better put this ship book into the cubby-hole,' he said

drops pattered on the leaves, only one or two got through to their platform. But Colin was worried.

'I'd better put this ship book into the cubby-hole,' he said. 'Hadn't I, Janet? Your father might be cross if it got wet.'

'Well he would,' said Janet. 'He's very careful about books. Put it at the back of

the cubby-hole, then it won't even get a drop.'

So the game was stopped while Colin tucked the big book away very carefully behind the little pile of food in the hole. The rain came down harder. It was rather fun to sit and listen to it pelting down on the leaves, and yet get hardly a drop on the platform.

By dinner-time the rain had stopped. 'We'd better make a dash for it now,' said Peter, trying to peer through the branches to see if there was any blue sky. 'Now what about our things? Do you suppose it's safe to leave them, after some of the biscuits and chocolate have been taken?'

'Quite safe,' said Pam, horrified at the thought of dragging everything down the tree to take home. 'If the squirrel —or whoever the thief was—didn't take the cushions or the mugs and things yesterday, it's not likely he will today. And we've only left a few biscuits.'

'Right,' said Peter. 'We'll just tie up the cushions in the rubber sheet and go. Scamper! We're coming!'

'Woof!' said Scamper, and they heard

him leaping up at the tree-trunk. He had been very bored in his 'sentry-box' all by himself.

They went down the tree carefully, because the rain had made parts of it rather slippery. Scamper gave them a most hilarious welcome.

They all went off to their homes, and alas, nobody noticed that Colin wasn't carrying the book of ships. He had forgotten all about it, and it was still tucked away in the cubby-hole half-way up the great big tree.

They went down the tree carefully because the rain had made parts of it rather slippery

35

Chapter 7
Windy Woods at Night

AFTER ANOTHER EXCITING DAY IN THE TREE-HOUSE THE SEVEN HAD RETURNED HOME TIRED AND HAPPY. BUT THAT NIGHT, AS HE WAS GETTING READY FOR BED, COLIN SUDDENLY REMEMBERED SOMETHING IMPORTANT...

THE BOOK! THE BOOK OF SHIPS! WHERE IS IT?

THEN, WITH A SHOCK, HE KNEW...

OH NO! I LEFT IT IN THAT CUBBY-HOLE IN THE TREE-HOUSE! SUPPOSE THAT SQUIRREL FINDS IT AND TEARS THE PAGES?—OR A STORM BLOWS RAIN INTO THE HOLE AND RUINS THE BOOK?—JANET'S FATHER WOULD BE FURIOUS!

COLIN KNEW HE HAD TO GO AND GET THE BOOK—BUT IT WAS ELEVEN O'CLOCK BEFORE THE HOUSE WAS QUIET AND HE COULD SLIP OUT INTO THE NIGHT...

HE HAD TO PASS PETER'S FARM ON THE WAY—AND WONDERED IF PETER WAS AWAKE...

I'M SURE HE'LL GO WITH ME, IF HE'S AWAKE. IT'S WORTH A TRY...

HE CREPT TO THE BACK OF THE FARMHOUSE AND BEGAN THROWING TINY STONES UP AT PETER'S WINDOW...

MOMENTS LATER...

WHAT WAS THAT?

THEY FOUND THE TREE WITHOUT ANY TROUBLE, THANKS TO PETER...

WAIT TILL I REACH THE PLATFORM, THEN I'LL SHINE THE TORCH SO YOU CAN SEE YOUR WAY UP.

RIGHT, NOW TO GET THE BOOK...

BUT...

I SAY! SOMEONE'S BEEN HERE AGAIN! EVERYTHING IS TOPSY-TURVY AND MUDDLED UP AS IF SOMEONE'S BEEN HUNTING FOR SOMETHING. FOOD, PROBABLY.

WELL, WE DIDN'T LEAVE MUCH. BLOW! IT CAN'T BE THAT SQUIRREL. IT MUST BE SOMEONE WHO HAS DISCOVERED OUR TREE-HOUSE. IS YOUR BOOK THERE?

YES, THANK GOODNESS. PETER, *WHO* COMES HERE? IT'S MADDENING!

SUDDENLY, A TINY SOUND NEARBY MADE THE BOYS JUMP...

DID YOU HEAR THAT? IT SOUNDED LIKE A TINY MEW - BUT THERE CAN'T BE A CAT UP HERE!

SHINE THE TORCH AROUND - SEE IF YOU CAN SEE ANYTHING...

L-LOOK, COLIN!

WHO-WHO'S THERE?

Chapter 8

Someone in the Tree-house

PETER suddenly made a grab for the two bare feet and caught hold of them. There was a yell, and the feet began to kick out. But Peter held them tightly.

'You come on down,' he said, angrily. 'Who are you? How dare you come to our tree-house and mess our things up. Come on down!'

'Let me go,' said a boy's voice, and then there came the mewing noise again, and to the two boys' surprise a small kitten leapt down to a nearby branch and stared at Peter and Colin with wide-open green eyes.

'A kitten!' said Colin. 'It must be that boy with the kitten! He did come back after all!'

'Don't pull me, don't pull me!' called the boy on the bough above. 'I'm slipping.'

Peter let go his feet. 'Come on down

boy put up his hand and stroked it gently. It began to purr.

Both Colin and Peter suddenly felt certain that the boy couldn't be terribly bad because he so obviously loved the kitten—and the kitten trusted him. They stared at the sullen boy.

'Go on—tell us,' said Peter, keeping the light of his torch full on the boy. 'We might be able to help you.'

'Will you let me stay here at night?' asked the boy. 'In case they find me. They know I'm somewhere in Windy Woods.'

'Who?' asked Peter. 'Tell us every-

then, and don't play the fool, because we're two to one,' he said.

The feet came down lower, then the legs, and then a thin body. Then came the whole boy, looking scared and white-faced.

'Sit down,' ordered Peter. 'Don't move. Now you just tell us what you're doing in our tree.'

The boy sat down. He looked up at them sulkily. He was thin and pale, and his hair wanted cutting.

'I only came here to hide,' he said. 'I've not done any harm, except to take a few biscuits last night. But if you'd been as hungry as I was, you'd have taken them too.'

'What are you hiding from?' asked Colin. 'Have you run away from home or something?'

'I shan't tell you anything,' said the boy. 'You might tell the police.'

'We shan't,' said Colin. 'At least, not if we can help it. Why should we tell the police anyhow?'

The kitten crept quietly back to the boy and cuddled into his coat. Colin and Peter saw that it had a bleeding leg. The

thing. What's your name, to begin with?'

'Jeff,' said the boy, still stroking the kitten. 'It all began when my mother went to hospital. I lived with her. My dad's dead, so there's only us two. But when Mum was taken to hospital I was sent to my Uncle Harry and my Aunt Lizzy.'

'Well, go on,' said Peter. 'Why did you run away?'

'I stayed there a week,' said Jeff, 'and

'Go on—tell us,' said Peter, keeping the light of his torch full on the boy

my mother didn't come out of hospital, and nobody would tell me anything. Suppose she never came out? What was I to do? All I had was my kitten.'

'Well, wouldn't your uncle and aunt have looked after you?' asked Peter.

'I didn't want them to,' said Jeff. 'They are bad. My mother always said so, and she knew. They've got bad friends, and they do bad things.'

'What do they do?' asked Peter.

'Oh—steal—and worse things,' said Jeff. 'They were all right to me, I mean they gave me food, and my aunt mended some of my clothes, but they were cruel to my kitten.'

Colin and Peter stared at Jeff in sympathy. Peter knew how he would have felt if someone had been unkind to Scamper. 'Did—did they hurt the kitten's leg where it's bleeding?' he asked.

Jeff nodded. 'Yes. Uncle kicked at it. It's not so bad now, but it was very bad at first. So that day I ran away, and took the kitten with me. I hid in an empty house, first, but they came after me. Then I came to this wood, and guessed you were up this tree, when your dog barked. So when you'd gone I climbed up.'

'I see,' said Peter. 'And ate our biscuits and chocolate. But why are your uncle and aunt bothering about you? They know you can go back when you want to.'

''Tisn't my aunt,' said Jeff. 'It's my uncle and his friend Mr Tizer. They're afraid I know too much.'

'Too much about what?' asked Colin.

'I saw Mr Tizer in the woods today with his dog'

'I used to sleep in the sitting-room,' explained Jeff. 'And one night I heard them talking about some plan they were making. I just heard a few things—but I couldn't make head or tail of them. I turned over to get more comfortable, and my uncle jumped up and accused me of listening.'

'Ah, and now that you've run away they're afraid you will tell someone what you heard,' said Colin. 'Did you hear much?'

'No—nothing to make any sense,' said Jeff. 'But they don't believe that, and they're after me. I saw Mr Tizer in the woods today with his dog. They're hunting me, and I'm scared. That's why I came up to your tree-house. Can't I stay?'

'Yes—you stay here for the night,' said Peter. 'Get out the cushions. Make yourself comfortable. And tomorrow we'll all come and see what's best to be done! Don't you worry—the Secret Seven will put things right!'

'My uncle jumped up and accused me of listening'

How to Play
Secret Sevenses

Do you wonder what sort of card game the Seven were playing in their tree-house in Chapter Five, when the wind kept flipping the cards off the platform? The game was a jolly good one, and a very old one too; it has been a favourite with boys and girls for many years. The Seven call it 'Secret Sevenses', but they are making no secret of it now! Below, they tell you how to play.

This is a game for two to seven players, although it is best played by three or four. Begin by giving a full pack of cards a good shuffle. One player takes the pack and begins to deal out the cards, one at a time, to the players, who should sit in a small circle. Each card must be placed face down and the dealer must keep dealing until each player has seven cards. The remaining cards are placed face down in a pile in the centre of the circle.

Players then pick up their seven cards and turn them over so they can see which ones they have—but they should be careful not to let others see their cards.

Each player looks at his cards to see if he has a 7. (There are four 7s in the pack, one in each set, or 'suit'—that is, a 7 of Clubs, 7 of Hearts, 7 of Spades and 7 of Diamonds.) The player on the left of the dealer begins the game. If he has a 7 he must lay this down, face up. If he does *not* have a 7 he must take a card from the top of the pile—but he must await his next turn before he can lay this or any other card.

Continuing to play in a clockwise direction, each player must lay a 7, if he has one; if not, he must try to add either a 6 or an 8, but only of the same suit—that is, if the 7 already laid is the 7 of Hearts, only the 6 or 8 of Hearts can be added to it. (The illustration on this page shows how the cards should be set out.)

Eventually, all four 7s will have been laid. The aim is to build on to these 7s until the four suits are complete. But no card can be laid unless the next card, either up or down the suit, has already been laid. For example, you cannot lay the 4 of Clubs unless the 5 of Clubs has been laid; neither can you lay the Jack of Spades if the 10 of Spades has not been laid. Each time a player is unable to lay a card he must pick up another from the pile.

So the game goes on, each player taking it in turn, until all the cards in the pile have been picked up and one player has no cards left. He is the winner!

If you want to go on to play a number of games, add up the value of the cards each player holds at the end of each game. (Aces count as one and Jacks, Queens and Kings count as 10.) The winner will be the player with the least number of points. If you wish, you can work out who comes second, third and so on; the higher a player's score, the lower his position. (If you *are* playing a number of games, be sure to give the pack a good shuffle before the start of each game, and appoint a new dealer for each game.)

Where is Scamper

Begin here →

| 1 | 2 | 3 | 4 | 5 | 6 | 7 |

45 | 44 | **43** Lose Secret Seven badge— go back 6 spaces | 42 | 41

46

47

48

49 Jeff offers to help— move on to 54

50

51

52 Lost in woods— go back 5 spaces

53

54 | **55** | **56** Secret Seven meeting gives you new ideas— take extra turn | **57** | **58** | **59** Old lady thinks she has seen Scamper— move on 6 spaces

69 Find dog biscuit by roadside— move on 4 spaces

70 | 71 | **72** Drop lunch pack from saddlebag— go back to 66

68

67

66

65

64 | **63** | **62** | **61** Stop for a rest— miss a turn

73

74

75

76

77

78 Local policeman offers to keep a look-out—take extra turn | **79** | **80**

Postman says he will check gardens— take extra turn

44

...amper has suddenly disappeared! Peter and Janet left him playing in the garden on Saturday ...rning, but when they went to call him, he was nowhere to be seen. They couldn't find him anywhere, ...they called in the rest of the Secret Seven to help them.
...ou can join in the search for Scamper, and discover which of the Secret Seven eventually finds him. ...m two to seven players can play this game. Each one chooses to be one of the Secret Seven and the ...nner is the member of the Seven who reaches Scamper first.
...ou will need a dice, and a counter or small button for each player. You must throw a six to start, and ...st get the exact number to finish the game.

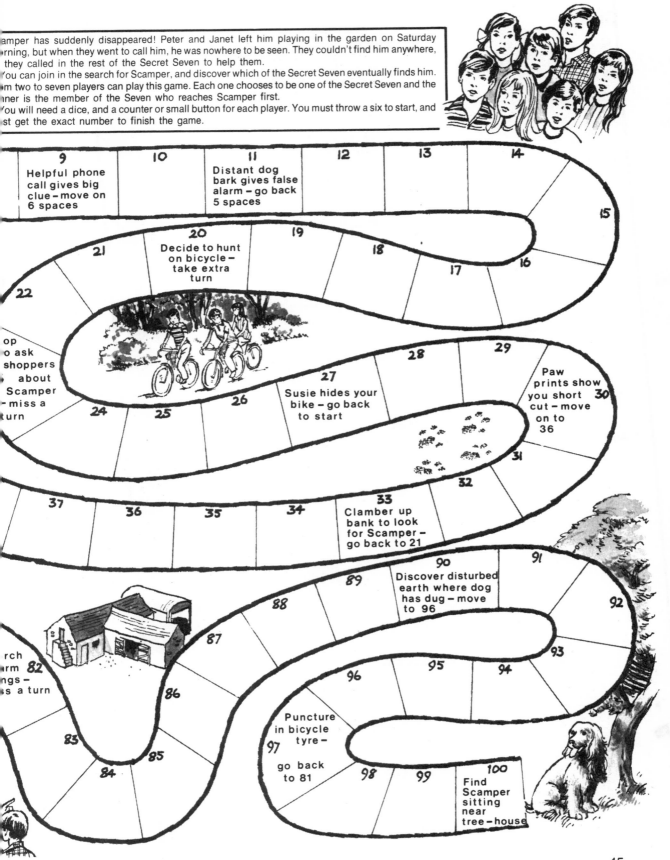

9 Helpful phone call gives big clue – move on 6 spaces
10
11 Distant dog bark gives false alarm – go back 5 spaces
12
13
14
15
16
17
18
19
20 Decide to hunt on bicycle – take extra turn
21
22
...op ...o ask shoppers ...about Scamper – miss a turn
24
25
26
27 Susie hides your bike – go back to start
28
29
30 Paw prints show you short cut – move on to 36
31
32
33 Clamber up bank to look for Scamper – go back to 21
34
35
36
37
...rch ...rm 82 ...ngs – ...s a turn
83
84
85
86
87
88
89
90 Discover disturbed earth where dog has dug – move to 96
91
92
93
94
95
96
97 Puncture in bicycle tyre – go back to 81
98
99
100 Find Scamper sitting near tree-house

Chapter 9

Another Meeting

NEXT MORNING, ALL THE SECRET SEVEN WERE EXCITED TO HEAR ABOUT JEFF, AND THAT THERE WAS TO BE A MEETING...

CAN WE TAKE SCAMPER WITH US? DO YOU SUPPOSE HE WOULD FRIGHTEN THE KITTEN?

NO, HE'S NICE WITH KITTENS. ANYWAY HE'LL BE ON GUARD DOWN BELOW, AND THE KITTEN WILL BE UP THE TREE WITH JEFF. I MUST REMEMBER TO TAKE A BOTTLE OF MILK, AND A SAUCER, AND SOME FISH.

GOOD THING WE HAD HADDOCK FOR BREAKFAST. I'LL WRAP A BIT UP IN GREASEPROOF PAPER. POOR LITTLE KITTEN. DO YOU SUPPOSE ITS LEG WILL BE ALL RIGHT? FANCY ANYONE KICKING A KITTEN!

PROMPTLY AT TEN O'CLOCK THE SECRET SEVEN MET AT THE FOOT OF THE TREE...

ADVENTURE!

YES, THAT'S THE PASSWORD. UP YOU GO.

HERE COME THE OTHERS.

ADVENTURE!

ADVENTURE! IS THAT BOY UP THERE?

YES. GOT YOUR BADGE ON? GOOD. RIGHT, WE'RE ALL HERE NOW. UP WE GO!

ON GUARD, SCAMPER, GOOD BOY!

HELLO, JEFF. HAD A GOOD NIGHT? HOW'S THE KITTEN?

47

ITS LEG IS MUCH BETTER. AND I SLEPT ALL NIGHT, EXCEPT WHEN THE WIND BLEW TOO HARD. I SAY— NOBODY WILL GIVE ME AWAY, WILL THEY?

NO FEAR! WE'RE A *SECRET* SOCIETY— THE SECRET SEVEN. WE HAVE OUR PASSWORD AND BADGES, AND WE HOLD MEETINGS. IF ANYTHING TURNS UP FOR US TO DO, WE DO IT.

HAVE THE OTHERS INTRODUCED THEMSELVES? THERE'S PAM, JACK, GEORGE, BARBARA AND JANET. YOU'VE MET COLIN.

HERE'S YOUR MILK, YOU TINY LITTLE THING— AND WE'VE SOME FISH FOR YOU. HAVE YOU GO IT, JANET?

THERE WE ARE. MY, YOU *ARE* A HUNGRY LITTLE FELLOW!

FOR A WHILE THE MEETING WAS FORGOTTEN AS THE CHILDREN GATHERED ROUND TO WATCH THE KITTEN. HE BROUGHT SMILES FROM EVERYONE— ESPECIALLY JEFF...

THANKS, EVERYONE. THANKS AN AWFUL LOT!

Do You Know Your Signs and Symbols ?

Answers on page 75

How are your powers of observation? If you want to be a junior detective you must have sharp eyes and a good memory. To test these important abilities, the Secret Seven have set the following quiz to see how much notice you take of things around you. The quiz is based on signs and symbols and is in three parts. Some of the symbols may be found in the home, some outside shops, garages and business offices, and some in newspapers and magazines or on advertising hoardings in the street. See how many you know, or can find.

Part 1: Initials
Some signs and symbols, like those opposite, include letters which stand for the name of the company or organisation which uses that symbol. How many of the following can you identify?

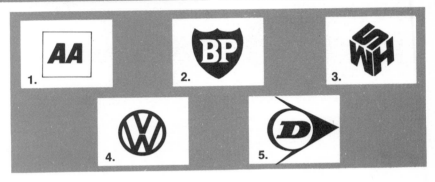

Part 2: Symbols
These signs and symbols are used without any letters. Do you know the names of the companies or organisations which use them?

Part 3: Hidden Names
In some signs and symbols the name of the company or organisation is used as part of the design. These symbols have had part of the name removed to make it more difficult to identify them. How many can you work out?

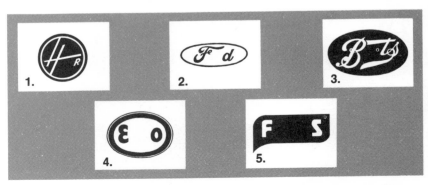

Make Your Own Rope Ladder

The Seven reach their tree-house by climbing on the tree's sturdy branches, but if the tree were in Peter and Janet's garden, where the Seven wouldn't have to worry about snoopers (like Jack's sister Susie!) discovering their meeting place, they could use a rope ladder. Peter has worked out simple instructions for you to make a rope ladder of your own, perhaps for use with your own tree-house (you would need a grown-up to make this for you). The rope ladder can be made quickly and easily—and quite cheaply. But it is wise to ask a grown-up to check your ladder once it is finished, just to make sure it is safe to use.

To begin with you will need two equal lengths of rope about $\frac{1}{2}$ cm thick. Nylon rope is best as this is strongest. (Do not use old or fraying rope, which might break and cause an accident.) To find out how much rope you need, measure the height to which you want your ladder to reach and double the length to allow for the knots and for plenty of rope for securing the ladder to the tree.

The rungs of the ladder can be made from strong metal or wooden rods. Broom-handles, cut to lengths of about 38 cm, would make ideal rungs, but ask a grown-up to saw the handles for you. How many broom-handles you need will, of course, depend on how many rungs you want in your ladder. These should be positioned about 23 cm apart.

To make your rope ladder you need to be able to *pull* on the two lengths of rope, so begin by tying the lengths (about 30 cm apart) to some fixed object several feet from the ground; a low branch of a tree would be ideal.

Leaving plenty of rope for securing to the tree when the ladder is finished, follow the instructions below for making the special knot into which you will slip the rungs.

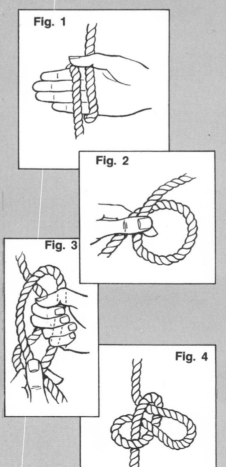

Fig. 1

Fig. 2

Fig. 3

Fig. 4

1. Take hold of one length of rope with your right hand and, with your left, wind the rope around your fingers.
2. With the thumb and first finger of your left hand, take hold of the rope and carefully remove your hand so that you are left with a loop.
3. Putting the fingers of your right hand through the loop, take hold of the rope.
4. Pull the rope back through the loop so that you form another, smaller loop.
5. Place one end of a rung through this loop so that the rung protrudes about 5 cm on the other side of the knot. (If the knot is not large enough for the rung, ease it open.)
6. Pull hard on the rope, tightening the knot around the rung.
7. Repeat on the other length of rope, ensuring that the rung is kept level; you don't want sloping rungs!
8. Do the same with each rung —and there's your rope ladder!

Chapter 10

Jeff Tries to Remember

PETER had also brought a jar of potted meat and a slab of cake for Jeff, and Colin had brought half a loaf and some butter. The boy took them hungrily, and didn't even wait to cut a slice of bread.

He tore at it with his teeth, and the others watched him, feeling shocked to see such hunger.

Janet gently took the bread from him, cut a large slice, buttered it and spread it thickly with potted meat. 'You'll like this better than mouthfuls of bread!' she said.

Jeff ate everything they had brought, except the biscuits they were keeping for mid-morning. He wiped his mouth on the sleeve of his jacket with a sigh.

'That was good,' he said. 'I can't tell you how good!'

The kitten had finished its meal now too, and was sitting beside Jeff, washing its face.

'It looks fatter already,' said Janet, stroking it. 'Poor little thing! Fancy kicking a baby like this! You wouldn't think there'd be anyone bad enough, would you?'

'Mr Tizer's *very* bad,' said Jeff. 'Worse than my uncle. He kicks me too.'

'We want you to tell us all you can,' said Peter, settling himself as comfortably as he could, with his back to the tree-trunk. 'We think we ought to try and find out what it was that Mr Tizer and your uncle were so afraid you had overheard. They must have been planning something wrong—something that ought to be stopped.'

Jeff stared at them. 'Stopped? Who's going to stop it? Not me. Nor you either. Nobody can stop Mr Tizer, not even the police. Anyway I don't know anything.'

'Jeff, you must try and think,' said Colin. 'You said you were asleep in the

'It looks fatter already,' said Janet

sitting-room on the sofa when your uncle and Mr Tizer were planning something. You said you woke up and turned over, and they were angry with you because they thought you'd heard what they were talking about. You *must* be able to remember *something*!'

'I can't,' said Jeff, looking sullen.

Peter felt sure he could if he really wanted to. 'You're afraid of Mr Tizer,' he said. 'That's why you won't try to remember. It's mean of you. We've been sorry for you and the kitten and helped you. Now you should help us. We'll see you don't come to any harm.'

Jeff stroked the kitten, and it purred loudly. 'Well—you've been jolly decent,' he said at last. 'And I'll try to remember what I overheard. But it doesn't make any sense to me, and it won't to you, either!'

'Never mind. Tell us,' said Colin.

Jeff frowned as he tried to remember. 'Let me see,' he began. 'I was asleep—and I woke up—and I heard their voices . . .'

'Yes. Go on,' said Peter.

'I don't know what they were talking about,' said Jeff. 'I was too sleepy to hear properly. I just heard a few things —things that don't make any sense.'

'What things?' asked Barbara, wishing she could jog Jeff and make him go faster in his story.

'Well—let's see—they talked about MKX,' said Jeff, frowning hard. 'Yes, I remember that clearly, MKX.'

'MKX?' said Jack. 'What in the world does that mean? Would it be a code-word for someone helping them in their plans?'

'I don't know,' said Jeff. 'But I do remember MKX. And I remember a date

'Never mind. Tell us,' said Colin

too—Thursday the 25th. They said that two or three times. That's next Thursday, isn't it?'

'Yes,' said Peter. 'It is. Perhaps that was the date of their next robbery or whatever they were planning to do! I say, this is exciting. Go on, Jeff. Remember something else!'

'Don't hurry me,' said Jeff. 'Else I shall remember wrong.'

There was a dead silence at once. No

Jeff frowned as he tried to remember

'**Anything else?**' **asked Peter.** '**You really are doing very well, Jeff**'

one wanted Jeff to 'remember wrong'!

'They spoke about someone too,' said Jeff, wrinkling his forehead. 'Let's see. Yes—Emma Lane. They kept on about Emma Lane, I do remember that.'

'Emma Lane? That's a good clue,' said Colin. 'We might be able to find out who she is. I've never heard of her.'

'Anything else?' asked Peter. 'You really are doing very well, Jeff. Think hard.'

Jeff was pleased. He thought again, going back in his memory to that night on the sofa, hearing the two men's voices again in his mind.

'Oh, yes!' he said suddenly, 'they said something about a red pillow. That puzzled me. A red pillow. I remember that.'

It puzzled the others too. A red pillow didn't seem to fit into anything. Who would have a red pillow, and what for?

'MKX. Thursday the 25th. Emma Lane. A red pillow,' said Peter. 'What a mix-up! I can't make head or tail of any plot with those four things in it. In fact, the only thing that is at all possible to follow up is the Emma Lane clue. Anything more, Jeff? Think, do think!'

'There was something about a grating,' said Jeff. 'Watching through a grating—yes, that was it! Does that help you at all?'

No, it didn't. It just added to all the mystery! How were the Secret Seven to tackle all that?

Chapter 11

Talking and Planning

GOOD BOY, SCAMPER! THEY WON'T BE BACK IN A HURRY!

GOOD DOG, NOW, ON GUARD AGAIN, SCAMPER, ON GUARD!

WOOF!

SCAMPER RETURNED TO HIS TREE, LOOKING PLEASED AND FEELING IMPORTANT!

BUT JEFF WAS STILL FRIGHTENED...

CHEER UP, JEFF. THEY'VE GONE NOW. BUT I WONDER HOW THEY GUESSED YOU WERE HERE?

I THINK IT'S BECAUSE OF THE KITTEN. THEY'VE ONLY GOT TO ASK IF ANYONE HAS SEEN A BOY WITH A KITTEN. SEVERAL PEOPLE IN THE WOOD HAVE SEEN ME ABOUT... THEY'LL GET ME IN THE END, I KNOW THEY WILL!

NO, THEY WON'T. NOW—WHAT ARE WE GOING TO DO ABOUT ALL THIS?

THE SEVEN TALKED AND TALKED—BUT SEEMED TO GET NOWHERE...

...BUT WHAT'S GOING TO HAPPEN ON IT, AND WHERE?

MKX— WHO OR WHAT IS THAT?

THE GRATING —WHERE'S THAT...?

THE 25TH— THAT'S A DEFINITE DATE...

THE RED PILLOW—THAT'S AN IMPOSSIBLE CLUE!

EMMA LANE— HOW CAN WE FIND OUT WHERE SHE LIVES?

...AND WHY IS SOMEONE GOING TO WATCH THROUGH IT?

Scamper's Story About the Spaniel

Photograph by Mark Hayes Fisher

What a wonderful guard dog Scamper is! How he saw off those two men in the chapter you have just read! And what a good companion he is for the Secret Seven. Do you remember what type of dog he is? You were told in Chapter One. He is a golden spaniel—although 'golden' describes only his colour; his proper breed name is a Cocker Spaniel. The Cocker is probably the best known of all the breeds in the Spaniel family. And what a big family it is! There are Field Spaniels, Springer Spaniels, Clumber Spaniels, Sussex Spaniels, Irish Water Spaniels, King Charles Spaniels, Brittany Spaniels, French Spaniels, Tibetan Spaniels . . . and more!

Of all these the Cocker Spaniel is without doubt the most popular breed. It makes an excellent pet and companion, being one of the friendliest and merriest of all dogs; watch one in action and you'll see that its tail never stops wagging! No wonder it topped Britain's popularity poll for more than twenty years!

Can you guess why the Spaniel is so named? It is because its ancestors were brought to Britain from Spain, probably by Julius Caesar's armies many hundreds of years ago. In those days the Spaniel was called either Espagnol, which is the French name for Spain, or Hispania, which is Latin.

But why *Cocker* Spaniel? Like many dogs, the Cocker Spaniel was named after the work it did. A reliable companion for the hunter, it was particularly good at scaring, or 'flushing', wood-

Photograph by Sally Anne Thompson

58

cock into the air. Today, though, few Cocker Spaniels are used as gun-dogs; they are mostly kept as pets.

One of the many reasons for its appeal as a pet is that it comes in such a variety of colours, including black, strawberry roan (strawberry and white), blue roan, liver—not forgetting red, or golden. And that brings us back to Scamper!

Photograph by Sally Anne Thompson

Photograph by Frank W. Lane

Above: **Misty loves to go to her local park in Bury, Lancashire, to play on the children's roundabout, swings and slide! Cocker Spaniels are very varied in colour, including orange and white *(top left)* and grey and white *(left)***

Far left inset: **A beautiful Springer Spaniel.** *Far left:* **This Cocker Spaniel puppy has soft eyes and a very wet, shiny nose**

Chapter 12

Emma Lane

IN THE HOPE OF SOLVING AT LEAST ONE OF THE STRANGE CLUES JEFF HAD GIVEN THEM, GEORGE AND JACK WENT TO THE LOCAL POST OFFICE TO FIND OUT IF THERE WAS ANYONE NAMED EMMA LANE IN THE VILLAGE...

STAMPS

I HOPE IT WON'T BOTHER YOU TO FIND OUT FOR US, BUT WE WANT TO KNOW WHERE SOMEONE CALLED EMMA LANE LIVES. IT'S RATHER IMPORTANT. CAN YOU POSSIBLY TELL US?

WELL, IT WILL TAKE ME A FEW MINUTES— BUT I'LL FIND OUT FOR YOU NOW.

DIRECTORY

YES, THERE *IS* AN EMMA LANE. MRS EMMA LANE, 1 CHURCH STREET. THAT MUST BE THE ONE YOU WANT.

OH, *THANKS!* 1 CHURCH STREET. THAT'S EASY TO REMEMBER!

WE'LL GO AND TELL PETER AFTER DINNER. THEN PERHAPS WE COULD ALL GO AND FIND OUT EXACTLY WHO EMMA LANE IS AND WHAT SHE DOES.

PETER AND JANET LISTENED EAGERLY TO THE NEWS...

WELL DONE! WE'LL GO STRAIGHTAWAY TO EMMA LANE'S AND SEE IF WE CAN FIND OUT ANYTHING AT ALL. SHE MIGHT KNOW MR TIZER, FOR INSTANCE.

YES, SHE MIGHT TELL US SOMETHING ABOUT HIM, AND THAT AWFUL UNCLE OF JEFF'S. SHALL WE GET THE OTHERS AND ALL GO TOGETHER?

NO, IT MIGHT LOOK A BIT ODD, SEVEN OF US ARRIVING TO TALK TO EMMA!

THEY WERE THERE IN MINUTES...

THERE IT IS. YOU GO, PETER. WE DID OUR BIT GOING TO THE POST OFFICE. I WOULDN'T KNOW *WHAT* TO SAY TO EMMA LANE!

ALL RIGHT. COME ON, JANET, YOU COME WITH ME.

ER — COULD YOU TELL ME IF MRS EMMA LANE IS IN?

WHO'S SHE? I'VE NEVER HEARD OF ANY EMMA LANE.

BUT THE POST OFFICE SAID SHE LIVED HERE. ISN'T THERE AN EMMA LANE HERE? WHAT ABOUT YOUR MOTHER?

MY MOTHER'S CALLED MARY MARGARET HARRIS, AND I'M LUCY ANN HARRIS.

WHO'S THAT, LUCY?

I DON'T KNOW. IT'S JUST TWO CHILDREN ASKING FOR SOMEONE WHO DOESN'T LIVE HERE.

HELLO. EXCUSE THE FLOUR, I'M MAKING CAKES. NOW WHO IS IT YOU WANT?

THEY WANT AN EMMA LANE — BUT SHE DOESN'T LIVE HERE, DOES SHE, MOTHER?

EMMA LANE? WHY, SHE'S YOUR GRANDMOTHER, SILLY!

I NEVER KNEW GRANNY'S NAME WAS EMMA. I NEVER HEARD ANYONE CALL HER EMMA LANE.

The Coded Message

The Secret Seven love writing secret, coded messages to one another, sometimes just for fun, but at other times so that Jack's mischievous sister Susie won't find out what their plans are! Here is a picture-code message which they have written specially for you. See if you can work out what it says, then ask your friends to try. (The message is given in full on page 75.)

Make a Miniature Garden

Do you like helping your parents in the garden? Peter and Janet do, and they so enjoy having plants and flowers around that they have made a miniature garden which Janet keeps by the window in her room. It's very easy to make and, unlike the garden outside, needs very little attention. Why not make one to brighten up your own room, or your mother's kitchen? Here Janet tells you all you need to know.

You will need
Seed tray (preferably polythene)
Newspaper or thick card
Seed compost or garden soil
Small mirror (or card covered with silver foil)
Small, flat stones and larger, rough stones
Moss or lawn grass
Various tiny-flowered plants
Pieces of conifer and heather

1. Place folded newspaper or sheet of thick card in the bottom of the seed tray to block off any holes. Three-quarters fill the tray with seed compost (this will keep down weeds) or garden soil free from insects and worms. Build up in one corner to form a mound.

2. Place the mirror (or card covered with silver foil) across the corner opposite the mound, pressing down gently into the compost or soil. This will be your garden pond.

3. Place the smooth, flat stones to make a gently winding path from the pond to the mound, pressing down to bed them in. Arrange the larger rough stones in one of the free corners to make a small rockery.

4. Transplant some tiny-flowered plants from the garden or hedgerows, bedding them in around the pond, at the foot of the rockery and on the mound. (Cultivated flowers: look out for Aubrietia, Alyssum, Violas, Campanulas and Ageratum. Wild flowers: keep an eye open for Speedwell, Pimpernel, Violets, Wood Sorrel and Cinquefoil. Lawn daisies also look pretty bedded in in small clusters.)

5. Moss is best for the lawn—it looks nicer than grass and doesn't grow quickly. But if you can't find enough moss, use lawn grass. Cut out (to a depth of about 1 cm) a small area from a spot where it won't be missed and lay it to fit around the pond, path, rockery and plants, pressing it well down all round.

6. Cut one or two pieces of conifer for trees and plant in the mound. These should stay green for a month or more, but after this will need replacing.

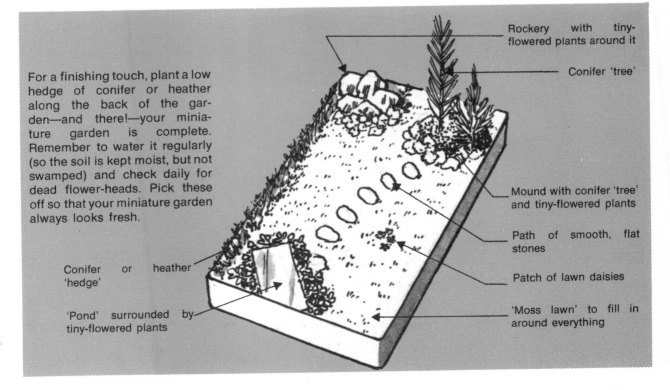

For a finishing touch, plant a low hedge of conifer or heather along the back of the garden—and there!—your miniature garden is complete. Remember to water it regularly (so the soil is kept moist, but not swamped) and check daily for dead flower-heads. Pick these off so that your miniature garden always looks fresh.

Rockery with tiny-flowered plants around it

Conifer 'tree'

Mound with conifer 'tree' and tiny-flowered plants

Path of smooth, flat stones

Patch of lawn daisies

'Moss lawn' to fill in around everything

Conifer or heather 'hedge'

'Pond' surrounded by tiny-flowered plants

Chapter 13

A Nasty Shock

DADDY was in to tea. Peter broke the news to him while he was spreading slices of bread and butter with honey.

'Daddy! The Secret Seven are in the middle of something again!'

Daddy and Mummy both looked up at once. 'You and your Secret Seven! What's up this time?' said Daddy. 'Nothing serious, I hope.'

'We don't know,' said Peter. 'But as two of the people in it are supposed to be really bad—and I think they are—then it might be serious. But although we know quite a lot, it's all so silly and muddled and difficult that we can't make head or tail of it. So we thought we'd better tell *you!*'

'Fire ahead,' said Daddy. 'I can

hardly wait to hear!'

'You're not to laugh, Daddy,' said Janet. 'The Secret Seven is a *proper* Society, and you know it's already done quite a lot of things.'

'I'm not really laughing,' said Daddy. 'Nor is Mummy. Tell us all about it.'

So Peter and Janet told the tale of their tree-house and Jeff and the kitten, and his wicked uncle and Mr Tizer, and all the curious collection of things that Jeff had remembered.

'Oh, *no*, Daddy,' said Janet at once. 'He *didn't* make it up. He really didn't'

Daddy ate his tea all the time. He listened, asking a few questions now and again. Mummy listened too, exclaiming once or twice that she thought the tree-house sounded very dangerous. At last the tale came to an end.

'It certainly wants looking into,' said Daddy. 'But if you want my opinion, I think that boy Jeff has made most of it up. He's feeling miserable, because his mother has gone into hospital, he doesn't like his uncle and aunt, he got into trouble with them, and ran away. And you were very kind to him, so he's made up a nice little tale!'

'Oh, *no*, Daddy,' said Janet at once. 'He *didn't* make it up. He really didn't. And the kitten *was* hurt. Somebody *had* kicked it!'

'Well, look here, go and fetch that boy Jeff and bring him here to me,' said Daddy. 'If there's anything in his story I'll soon find out, and if there *is* any funny business going on we'll find that out too. He can tell us the address of his uncle, and the police can go and see if there's anything in his tale.'

'He doesn't want the police to be told,' said Peter.

'Of course he doesn't, if he's made up the tale!' said Daddy. 'Now you go and fetch him. Tell him I shan't bite his head off. As for all the things he says he remembers hearing when he was half-asleep, well, *I* think he dreamt them! Don't look so upset, both of you. When you get a bit older you'll learn not to believe all the tales people tell you!'

'But Daddy, he was speaking the truth, I'm sure he was,' said Janet, almost in tears.

'Right. Then we'll certainly do something to help him,' said Daddy. 'Go and get him now. I'll finish a job I'm on and be ready as soon as you get back.'

Peter and Janet set off rather gloomily to the tree-house. It was very, very damping to have Daddy and Mummy so certain that Jeff was a fraud. *They* didn't think he was. Well, now Jeff would have to go with them and tell Daddy everything. He would probably be so scared that he wouldn't say a word!

'I hope Jeff *will* come back with us,' said Peter, suddenly thinking that it might be very, very difficult to get him to climb down the tree if he didn't want to. They said no more till they got to the tree.

Peter called up. 'Jeff! Come on down!

We've got something to tell you.'

Nobody answered. Peter called again. 'JEFF! It's me, Peter. Come on down. There's nobody here but me and Janet. It's important.'

There was no reply. But wait—yes, there was! A tiny little mew sounded from up above. The kitten!

'The kitten's there,' said Peter. 'So Jeff must be there too. I wonder if he's all right? I'll go up and see.'

Up he went. He climbed up on to the platform which was still strewn with

Peter and Janet set off rather gloomily to the tree-house

Peter took it and read it

cushions. The kitten ran to him, mewing.

There wasn't a sign of Jeff! Peter called again and peered upwards, thinking the boy might have climbed higher. No—he wasn't there either! Then he caught sight of a piece of paper stuck into a crevice of the tree-trunk. Peter took it and read it.

'They've found me,' said the note.

'They say they'll come up and throw the kitten down the tree if I don't climb down to them. They would too. Take care of the kitten—and thanks for everything. Jeff.'

Peter slithered down the tree so quickly that he grazed his hands and knees. He held out the paper to Janet. 'Look at that! They've found him. They must have come back again, guessing he might be up here, with Scamper barking round like that. Poor Jeff!'

Janet looked upset and alarmed. 'Oh dear—*now* what are we to do? We don't even know where Jeff lives. We can't find out anything, or help him. Oh look, that poor little kitten is coming down the tree all by itself!'

Peter lifted it down. It mewed. 'We'll look after you all right,' he said. 'Where has your master gone to? That's what *we'd* like to know!'

Chapter 14

George Gets an Idea

PETER and Janet went home, the kitten cuddled against Peter. Daddy was waiting for them.

'Well—where's the boy, Jeff?' he said.

'He's gone,' said Peter, and showed his father the note.

'You won't hear of *him* again,' said Daddy. 'I tell you, it was just a made-up tale. Forget it! Ask your mother if you can keep the kitten, though we don't really want another cat. I don't think

much of the boy, deserting the kitten like that!'

'He didn't, Daddy,' said Janet, trying not to cry. 'He *had* to leave it. Those men were cruel.'

Daddy went away to his work. Peter and Janet looked at one another. Daddy was so often right about things. Perhaps he was right about this too. Perhaps Jeff *had* been a fraud, and made up a tale to tell them.

'What are we going to do?' asked Janet, wiping her eyes. Peter considered.

'We'll have to give it up,' he said. 'We can't very well go against what Daddy says, and we *know* we can't do anything ourselves, because we don't understand what any of the things Jeff remembered can possibly mean. And now Jeff is gone, and we don't know where, we can't even get him to tell his tale to anyone!'

'We'll have to call a meeting and tell the others,' said Janet, gloomily. 'They won't like it. It sounded so exciting at first, now it's just a silly make-up. And I liked Jeff, too.'

'So did I,' said Peter. 'Let's write notes and slip them into the letter-boxes to tell the others there will be a meeting

70

tomorrow. Down in the shed, I think, for a change.'

The notes were written and delivered. At ten o'clock the next morning the Seven collected together in the shed. The password 'Adventure' seemed most disappointing to Janet and Peter now that there *was* no adventure.

'I've got gloomy news,' said Peter. 'We told Daddy everything, and he didn't believe it. He told us to fetch Jeff, and promised to listen to his story—but Jeff was gone!'

Peter produced the note and everyone read it solemnly

Everyone was startled. 'Gone!' said Jack. 'Where?'

Peter produced the note and everyone read it solemnly. 'We've got the kitten,' said Peter. 'And that's all that's left of Jeff and his peculiar tale.'

'So we can't go on with anything,' said George, in dismay. 'I was just getting all worked up about it, thinking we were in for another excitement.'

'I know. But we were wrong,' said

Peter. 'This affair is closed. We can't go any further or find out anything more. It's our first failure.'

It was a very gloomy meeting indeed. Everyone felt very flat. They wondered where Jeff was. Had he *really* cheated them and told them a made-up tale? It was very difficult to believe.

'We saw Mr Tizer and Jeff's uncle, you know,' said Colin, suddenly. '*They* couldn't have been made up.'

'We've only got Jeff's word for it that they were his uncle and Mr Tizer,' Peter reminded him. 'He certainly said they were, but for all we know they might have been two woodcutters, or even poachers. They looked pretty nasty, anyway.'

There was a silence. 'All right,' said George at last. 'It's finished. We don't do anything more. Are we going to the tree-house today?'

'I don't feel like it somehow, this morning,' said Janet. 'Does anyone? I feel disappointed and rather cross.'

Everyone laughed. Janet was hardly

ever cross. Colin patted her on the back. 'Cheer up! We'll soon get over it. And anyway, finished or not, I'm still going to keep my eyes open! Who knows—I might meet Emma Lane walking down the street, carrying a red pillow embroidered with the letters MKX!'

That made everyone roar with laughter. They said good-bye and went off feeling more cheerful.

'What's the date?' said George to Colin, as they went down the lane together. 'Wednesday the 24th, isn't it? Well, it's tomorrow that things were supposed to happen, according to Jeff.'

'He probably made up the date,' said Colin. 'What are we going to do this morning? We've plenty of time left.'

'Let's go down to the canal,' said

'Meet me in that road that goes under the railway bridge'

George. 'We may see some barges going along. I like the canal, it's so long and straight and quiet.'

'I like it too,' said Colin. 'I'll go and get my boat. You get yours too. Meet me in that road that goes under the railway bridge, down by the canal.'

'What road?' asked George, but Colin had already gone. George raised his voice. 'Colin! What road do you mean? I don't want to miss you!'

'You know the road, idiot,' yelled back Colin. 'It's EMBER LANE!'

Colin was so far away by this time that it was difficult to catch what he said. It sounded like 'EMMA LANE.' George stood rooted to the spot. Ember Lane. *Emma Lane*. Jeff might have misheard what his uncle had said—it was probably Ember Lane he meant, not Emma Lane! They sounded so much the same. EMBER LANE!

'It might be that. It might be,' said George to himself in excitement. 'We'll have a jolly good look round Ember Lane—just *in case*!'

73

How Do You Rate

Would *you* make a good Secret Seven member? If you're sharp-eyed, quick-witted and have 'staying power', probably you would, for these are the three most important factors which each member of the Seven possesses. On these pages are some simple tests designed to assess your abilities. See how well you can do, remembering that each member of the Seven passed these tests with flying colours! Check your answers on the next page.

F	I	S	H
F	I	S	T
C	H	I	P

FISH FUN

Here's a test to make your mouth water! Can you change the word FISH into CHIP by altering one letter in FISH to make another word, and then altering one letter in the second word, and so on? To start you off, the first word change has been written in. Score one point for each of the remaining six words to be inserted.

FIGURE IT OUT!

How old is this man? If you add up all the numbers from which he is made you will find out. Score ten points for the correct answer.

TREE TEST

The answers to the clues below are all words which end with the sound 'tree', but are actually spelt 'try'. For example, if the clue read 'This tree is found in some cranes', the answer would be 'Gantry'. See how many you can work out. Score one point for each one you get right.

1. You'll find food in this tree.
2. This tree stands on guard.
3. You couldn't make a pie without this tree.
4. You need timber and tools to practise this tree.
5. This tree usually takes place in a laboratory.
6. Much work is carried out in this tree.
7. This tree has to be woven with materials.
8. Knights in armour were known for this tree.
9. You clean your teeth to avoid this tree.
10. Creative people—painters, writers, actors—use this tree.

TITLE TEASER

Can you re-arrange the following pairs to form the titles of ten well-known books or films? Score one point for each correct answer.

1. Mary Crusoe
2. Treasure Beauty
3. Little Dolittle
4. Peter Dick
5. Robinson Book
6. Black Poppins
7. Moby Twist
8. Doctor Women
9. Jungle Pan
10. Oliver Island

NUMBERS GAME

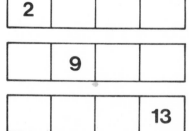

Write the numbers, 3, 4, 5, 6, 7, 8, 10, 11 and 12 in the blank squares so that each row adds up to 30. Score five points for each correct row.

How Did You Do

TITLE TEASER
1. Mary Poppins. 2. Treasure Island. 3. Little Women. 4. Peter Pan. 5. Robinson Crusoe. 6. Black Beauty. 7. Moby Dick. 8. Doctor Dolittle. 9. Jungle Book. 10. Oliver Twist.

FIGURE IT OUT!
The man is 60.

FISH FUN
Fish, fist, fast, cast, cost, coat, chat, chap, chip.

TREE TEST
1. Pantry. 2. Sentry. 3. Pastry. 4. Carpentry. 5. Chemistry. 6. Industry. 7. Tapestry. 8. Gallantry. 9. Dentistry. 10. Artistry.

NUMBERS GAME

2, 10, 7, 11.

3, 9, 6, 12.

4, 8, 5, 13.

SCORE RATINGS
Maximum score of 51 points.

46-51 Excellent: you would make a good Secret Seven member.

35-45 Good: you have the potential; work just a little harder.

25-34 Fair: there's plenty of room for improvement, although you *could* qualify; more effort is needed.

DOMINOES PUZZLE
(page 29)

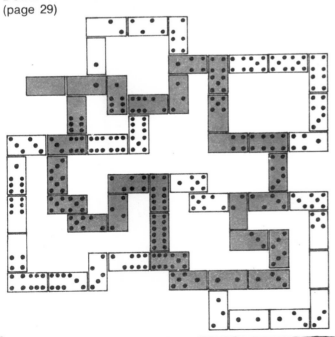

CODED MESSAGE
(page 63)

Why not form your own secret society with your friends? You can have lots of fun solving puzzles and helping people. But don't forget to make special badges and membership cards, just like the Seven's.

SIGNS AND SYMBOLS (page 49)
Part 1: 1. Automobile Association. 2. British Petroleum. 3. W. H. Smith. 4. Volkswagen. 5. Dunlop.

Part 2: 1. British Rail. 2. World Wildlife Fund. 3. National Westminster Bank. 4. Save the Children Fund. 5. Shell.

Part 3: 1. Hoover. 2. Ford. 3. Boots. 4. Esso. 5. Findus.

Chapter 15

The Red Pillow

...AND ON THE WAY HOME PEEPED AGAIN THROUGH THE WAREHOUSE GRATING.

WE'D BETTER TELL OLD PETER. LET'S GO ALONG THIS AFTERNOON AND TELL HIM. HE OUGHT TO KNOW, I THINK, EVEN THOUGH THERE MAY BE NOTHING IN IT.

RIGHT. I'LL MEET YOU THERE.

PETER WAS MOST INTERESTED...

THAT'S BRIGHT OF YOU. EMMA LANE. EMBER LANE. ANYONE COULD MISHEAR THAT QUITE EASILY. BUT I DON'T THINK SO MUCH OF THE GRATING. THERE ARE GRATINGS EVERYWHERE

NOT IN EMBER LANE. WE LOOKED, AND THAT'S THE ONLY ONE.

HMMM. PERHAPS JANET AND I WILL GO ALONG AND HAVE A LOOK AT EMBER LANE THIS AFTERNOON. AND THE GRATING...

AND SO...

COLIN WAS RIGHT. THIS IS THE ONLY ONE IN EMBER LANE.

YES, BUT IT DOESN'T TELL US MUCH.

EVEN IF WE DECIDED THAT THIS WAS THE GRATING THROUGH WHICH MR TIZER OR SOMEONE WAS GOING TO WATCH, WHY SHOULD THEY WANT TO WATCH? AND WHAT? IT'S NO CRIME TO PEER THROUGH A GRATING.

THEY MIGHT WANT TO WATCH UNSEEN FOR SOMETHING OR SOMEONE, SO THAT THEY COULD SIGNAL HIS COMING TO SOMEBODY WAITING TO POUNCE.

77

YES! THAT'S EXACTLY WHAT THEY *MIGHT* DO! BUT WHAT COULD THEY SEE FROM HERE? LET'S STAND WITH OUR BACKS TO THE GRATING AND SEE IF WE CAN SPOT WHAT WOULD BE WITHIN THEIR SIGHT.

WELL, THERE'S THAT WAREHOUSE OPPOSITE, AND THE LAMP-POST...

AND THE PAVEMENT, AND THAT RED PILLAR-BOX. YES, I'M SURE THAT RED PILLAR-BOX COULD BE SEEN TOO.

SUDDENLY JANET CAUGHT HER BREATH...

PETER! PETER, THE RED PILLOW!

THE RED PILLOW? WHERE?

OH, JANET—JANET! I SEE WHAT YOU MEAN! IT WASN'T A RED *PILLOW* THAT JEFF HEARD, IT WAS RED *PILLAR-BOX*. AND THERE IT IS!

WE'RE GETTING SOMEWHERE! JEFF *DID* HEAR SOMETHING. HIS TALE WASN'T MADE UP.

NO. BUT BECAUSE HE WAS HALF ASLEEP WHEN HE HEARD THE MEN TALKING, HE DIDN'T HEAR PROPERLY.

IF ONLY WE COULD FIND WHAT MKX IS — BUT WE CAN'T. I EXPECT ALL THE MEN IN MR TIZER'S GANG HAVE NUMBERS OR LETTERS.

BUT WE'RE CERTAINLY PUTTING A FEW OF THE JIGSAW PIECES TOGETHER. LET'S GO AND TELL THE OTHERS!

Chapter 16

And Now MKX

EVERY member of the Secret Seven felt excited when they heard the latest news. They thought that Janet had been very clever in realizing that the red pillow was a mistake for red pillar-box.

Barbara thought for a moment and then said that she wondered if the man watching behind the grating might be waiting to signal to someone when the postman came to empty the box.

'Someone might be waiting to steal the letters from him,' she said.

'That's an idea,' said Peter. 'But there isn't much point in stealing ordinary letters. They're not worth anything!'

'That's true,' said Jack. 'It's sacks of registered parcels and letters that are usually stolen. They're worth something. But not ordinary letters. I don't somehow think the watcher is watching the pillar-box, he's probably watching for someone waiting there, or passing it.'

'Is it worth telling Daddy all this, Janet, do you suppose?' said Peter, after the Seven had discussed everything thoroughly. 'After all—it's tomorrow *something* has been planned to happen. We haven't much time left.'

'Well—we might tell him this evening,' said Janet. 'Let's wait till then. We might think of something else important. I don't think Daddy will change his mind about things just because we've discovered that a red pillar-box can be watched through a grating in Ember Lane.'

'It does sound rather silly put like that,' said Peter. 'Well—we'll wait till this evening. Good-bye till then.'

But before they could tell their father of their latest ideas, Pam came dashing into the garden to find Peter and Janet. Barbara was just behind.

They found Peter and Janet watering their gardens. Pam flung herself on them.

'Peter! Janet! What do you think? We've seen MKX!'

Janet dropped her watering-can, startled. Peter stared in excitement.

'Who is he? Where did you see him?'

'It isn't a he. It's a van!' said Barbara.

Janet dropped her watering-can

'Pam and I were going home together, when we saw a post-office van standing near a pillar-box—you know, a mail-van, painted red.'

'And its letters were MKX!' cried Pam. 'MKX 102. What do you think of that? We couldn't believe our eyes when we saw it was MKX. I'm sure that's what Jeff meant—the mail-van, MKX.'

'But—but there must be plenty of cars with the letters MKX,' said Peter. 'Plenty.'

'Not in one place,' said Pam. 'I don't ever remember seeing MKX in our town before. I notice car numbers, because I want to see if I can spot a Z something someday. I haven't yet. Peter! That van *must* be the MKX those men spoke about when Jeff was half asleep.'

Peter sat down on a garden-seat. 'I think you're right,' he said. 'Yes—I think you must be right. It's all beginning to fit in. Wait now, let's puzzle it out.'

He sat up and thought, frowning hard. 'Yes, perhaps a mail van goes into Ember Lane, with a few sacks of registered parcels inside. The postman gets out of his van to go across to the red pillar-box to collect the letters.'

'Yes! YES!' cried Pam. 'And someone is watching through the grating to see when he is unlocking the pillar-box, with his back to the van, and signals to the others who are waiting out of sight somewhere . . .'

'And at once they see the signal, rush to the van, and drive it off before the postman can get back to it!' cried Janet, taking the words out of Pam's mouth.

They all sat and looked at one another, their eyes shining. They felt

He pursed up his mouth and gave his head a little scratch

breathless. Had they solved everything, or was it just too clever to be true?

'Well, I shall certainly tell Daddy now,' said Peter, thrilled. 'What a bit of luck you noticed the letters on that mail-van, Pam and Barbara. Good work! We're a jolly fine Secret Society, I think. Successes every time!'

'And we thought this one was a failure!' said Janet. 'Look, there's Daddy. Come and tell him now.'

So Peter's father was soon surrounded by four excited children, determined to make him believe that what they had discovered REALLY MATTERED!

He listened carefully. He pursed up his mouth and gave his head a little scratch, looking with twinkling eyes at the children. 'Well, well, this is rather a different tale this time. Most ingenious! Yes, I'll do something about it.'

He went indoors and rang up the Inspector of Police, and asked him to come along. 'I've a curious tale to tell you,' he said. 'You may or may not believe it, but I think you ought to hear it.'

And before ten minutes had passed the kindly-faced Inspector was sitting in the garden, listening solemnly to the children's tale.

He glanced at Peter's father when they had finished. 'This is important,' he said. 'There have been too many mail-van robberies lately. We'll catch the ring-leaders this time, thanks to the valiant Secret Seven!'

Chapter 17

Top Secret

HE got up to go. The children pressed round him. 'Tell us what you are going to do! Do, do tell us!'

'I'm going to discuss the whole matter with other people,' said the Inspector, smiling down at the four children. 'You've not given me much time to make preparations, you know! According to you, it's all fixed for tomorrow!'

'How shall we know what's going to happen?' asked Pam. 'It's *our* affair this —can't we see what's going to happen?'

'I'll let you know tomorrow, at ten o'clock,' said the big Inspector, twinkling at them. 'Call a meeting of your Secret Society down in the shed, and I'll be there to report to you!'

There was such excitement that evening among the Secret Seven that their parents thought they would never get them to bed. Colin, George and Jack were all told by the other four, and spent a wonderful time thinking how clever they had been.

'Well, we'll meet down in the shed at ten tomorrow,' said Colin. 'Passwords, and everything, and you all realize, of course, that not one single word of what the Inspector tells us is to be told to ANYONE ELSE.'

'Of course,' said everyone.

At five to ten they had all arrived at the shed except the Inspector. He came promptly at ten o'clock.

'Have to let him in without the password,' said Peter. But Janet called out loudly. 'Password, please!'

The Inspector grinned to himself outside the shed. 'Well,' he said, 'I don't know it, but there's one word that seems to me to be a very good password for you

In went the Inspector and was given a large box to sit on

at the moment, and that is—ADVENTURE!'

'Right!' shouted everyone in delight, and the door opened. In went the Inspector and was given a large box to sit on. He beamed round at them all.

'This is SECRET,' he said. 'Top secret. We've made inquiries, and we think it is possible that a robbery may be planned this evening when the postman drives up in his mail-van to make the seven-thirty collection of letters from the red pillar-box in Ember Lane. At that time of the evening he has on board his van some sacks of registered letters.'

'Oooooh!' said Pam. 'Just what we thought!'

'Now what we are going to do is this,'

said the Inspector. 'A postman will drive up as usual with the mail-van. He will park it in the usual place. He will go across to the pillar-box and unlock it, with his back to the van.'

'Yes,' said everyone, hanging on to the Inspector's words. 'What next?'

'Well, the watcher behind the grating will probably signal to others waiting opposite in hiding,' said the Inspector. 'They will rush to the van, jump into the driver's seat, two of them probably, and drive it away.'

'But, will you let them do that?' said Pam. 'With all the sacks inside!'

'The sacks won't be inside, my dear,' said the Inspector. 'But six fine policemen will, and WHAT a shock for the two men when they park the mail-van somewhere lonely and go to unlock the van door.'

'Oh!' cried the Seven, and gazed at the Inspector in delight.

'And the man signalling behind the grating will find two policemen waiting for him in the passage outside the underground room,' said the big Inspector. 'Very interesting; don't you think so?'

'Please—PLEASE can we be somewhere and watch?' asked Peter. 'After all, if it hadn't been for us you wouldn't have known anything about this.'

'Well now, you listen,' said the Inspector, dropping his voice low and making everything sound twice as exciting. 'There's a warehouse called Mark Donnal's in Ember Lane, and it's got a back entrance in the road behind, Petton Road. Nobody will say anything if seven children go in one by one, and make their way to a window overlooking

Janet hugged it

Ember Lane at the front of the warehouse. In fact, I wouldn't be surprised if there isn't someone there to show you the very room you want!'

Every single one of the Secret Seven wanted to hug the big Inspector, but as he got up at that moment, they couldn't. They beamed in delight at him.

'Thank you! It's marvellous of you! We'll be there, if our parents let us.'

'I think you'll find that will be all right,' said the Inspector, and off he went.

'WELL!' said Peter, looking round. 'This is wonderful. Seats in the very front row.'

'Yes. But we shan't be able to see the best bit of all, when the men open the van, and out come the policemen!' said Jack.

'Never mind, we'll see plenty!' said Peter. 'I wonder where Jeff is? I suppose that awful Mr Tizer took him away and locked him up somewhere till the raid should be over. I wonder what will happen to poor old Jeff?'

'Mew,' said the kitten, who was on Janet's knee. Its leg was healed now, and it was a fat, amusing little thing. Janet hugged it.

'I expect poor Jeff misses you,' she said. 'Never mind, maybe we'll be able to do something for Jeff if he's found, and you can go back to him.'

'I wish tonight was here,' said George, getting up. 'It'll never come!'

But it did come, and it brought a most exciting evening with it!

Wonderful Waterways

Have you ever sailed a boat on a canal, like the one you see on the next page? And have you ever wondered why canals were built? They are not *natural* waterways, like rivers; they were dug out of the land by teams of hard-working men and filled with water many, many years ago. They were built for a special purpose: to provide routes along which coal, bricks, timber and other heavy, bulky goods could be carried from the mines and factories. Many canals also ran regular passenger services, including a 'market boat' which took housewives to market once a week.

People weren't in such a hurry in those days, so nobody minded that the boats—called barges —moved quite slowly, pulled either by horses or men, who walked along a narrow 'towing path' beside the canal. Later, steam-driven canal boats were used, but these were still very

slow compared with today's goods vehicles.

At one time there were more than four thousand miles (6436 km) of waterways (including rivers) in use in Britain, but when the railways began to be built, mine and factory owners started sending their goods by rail, because this was often cheaper and quicker than using the canals. The waterways were used less and less until eventually many canals were so neglected that they became unusable.

But there is a happy ending to the story of our canals. Thanks to the many people who care about our waterways, many of our old canals have been mended and restored so that today there are over two thousand miles (3218 km) of waterways in use, and other stretches are being reclaimed and rebuilt all the time. Nowadays, though, the canals are not used a great deal for carrying

Above: **The 'Bingley Five Rise', on the Leeds and Liverpool Canal**

Top: **Fishing on the calm waters of the Shropshire Union Canal**

Above: A cruiser glides into the chamber of an Oxford Canal lock

Right: A hired cruiser in Buckby top lock, Northamptonshire

goods; instead they have a new rôle to play in providing lovely, quiet places where people can go to enjoy themselves, cruising, canoeing or fishing, or rambling along their towing paths. No wonder they are called 'wonderful waterways'!

Want to know more?
If you would like more information about the 'wonderful waterways', write to:
British Waterways Board, Melbury House, Melbury Terrace, London NW1 6JX.
Inland Waterways Association, 114 Regent's Park Road, London NW1 8UQ.

Above right: Part of the re-opened Ashton Canal in Greater Manchester

Right: The Stretton Aqueduct—part of the Shropshire Union Canal

All photographs by British Waterways Board

A Picture to Colour

The old canal is a peaceful place;
The narrow boats come sailing.
Dobbin the horse pulls them along
And the bargeman stands a-waving.
Colin and George sail their boats
And enjoy the scene around them;
So the picture here can be coloured now
With paint or crayon or felt-pen.

Chapter 18
An Exciting Finish

GRATEFUL FOR THE INFORMATION WHICH WOULD HELP THE POLICE CATCH MR TIZER AND HIS FRIENDS, THE INSPECTOR TOLD THE SEVEN THEY WOULD BE ABLE TO WATCH THE EXCITEMENT FROM A ROOM OVERLOOKING EMBER LANE. BY HALF PAST SIX THAT EVENING, THE LAST OF THE CHILDREN HAD ARRIVED...

PETTON ROAD

MARK DONNAL'S WAREHOUSE

IN YOU COME. THE OTHERS ARE ALREADY HERE. I'LL SHOW YOU THE WAY.

WE'VE GOT A MARVELLOUS VIEW OF THE RED PILLAR-BOX. WE SHALL SEE EVERYTHING.

OH GOOD! IS THE SIGNALLER DOWN BEHIND THE GRATING YET?

YES, HE'S THERE ALL RIGHT. WE'VE WATCHED HIM GO INTO THE UNDERGROUND ROOM, COMPLETE WITH WHITE HANDKERCHIEF FOR SIGNALLING. THERE ARE NOW TWO POLICEMEN IN A CUPBOARD OUTSIDE THE DOOR, WAITING!

THE NEXT HOUR SEEMED TO DRAG BY, BUT THEN, ALL OF A SUDDEN...

MKX 102

AT THE SIGNAL TWO MEN LEAPT INTO THE STREET AND SPRINTED AT TOP SPEED TO THE VAN...

SECONDS LATER...

GOLLY, WHAT EXCITEMENT! BUT THE POSTMAN DIDN'T EVEN LOOK SURPRISED!

THAT'S RIGHT. HE'S IN THE SECRET TOO—HE KNEW WHAT TO EXPECT.

LISTEN TO THE NOISE! I BET THAT'S THE SIGNALLER BEING CAUGHT!

IT WAS! HE HAD WALKED OUT OF THE ROOM STRAIGHT INTO THE ARMS OF THE LAW!

WELL DONE, MEN. RIGHT, AWAY WITH HIM.

BUT THE EVENING'S EXCITEMENT WASN'T YET FINISHED! HALF AN HOUR LATER...

RIGHT, STAND BY, MEN. LET'S GET THESE CULPRITS AWAY TO THE STATION QUICKLY.

GOT THEM NICELY! THEY MUST HAVE PARKED NEARBY, OPENED THE VAN, AND GOT THE SURPRISE OF THEIR LIVES! AND HERE THEY ARE, BACK AGAIN TO TALK TO THE CHIEF!

AND AFTER ALL THE ACTION, A LIFT HOME IN A POLICE CAR!

GOLLY, WHAT A SUPER END TO AN EXCITING DAY!

YES, AND YOU'RE ALL INVITED TO OUR HOUSE FOR SUPPER!

AND WAITING AT PETER AND JANET'S HOUSE WAS ANOTHER SURPRISE...

JEFF!

DOs and DON'Ts of of Kitten Care

Would you like a kitten like Jeff's? Or perhaps you already have one? One thing you will have learned already is that a kitten needs caring for, and affection and protection like Jeff showed go a long way towards making a kitten feel secure. But there's lots more to kitten care, and here Jeff spells out some of the things you ought to know about choosing a kitten and looking after it, set out in a helpful DOs and DON'Ts way.

Choosing your kitten

Do gently feel the stomach of the kitten you are considering buying; it should be firm and rubbery, not swollen or flabby.
Do check the kitten's ears; they should be clean and odour-free.

Photographs by Syndication International

Do look at the eyes; they should be clear and bright, not runny.
Do feel the coat; it should have no rough patches, which could be sores, but might be just scratches from playing. Check.
Do pick a playful kitten; it will make a good pet.
Don't pick the kitten which appears to be the 'boss' of the litter; it won't make a good companion.
Don't pick up a kitten the wrong way; the correct way is to put one hand under the chest with the other supporting the back legs.
Don't buy a kitten which is less than eight weeks old. Check inside its mouth; a kitten of eight weeks will have a full set of small, sharp teeth.

Your kitten's new home

Do give your kitten some warm milk (or condensed milk or warm custard) as soon as you get it home.
Do let your kitten explore its new home, sniffing around until it is satisfied it is safe. (Cats rely heavily upon their sense of smell; watch how they sniff at food before eating it.)
Do make a cosy sleeping place for your kitten—an old blanket or pullover placed in a cat-basket (or cardboard box) would be sufficient.
Do remember that for its first few nights in its new home a kitten will miss its mother and brothers and sisters, so place a covered hot-water bottle (warm not hot) in its bed; it will be comforted by this. It may also appreciate having something by its side which bears the scent of its new owner, such as a slipper. This will help it feel safe when left alone.
Do let your kitten sleep when it wants to. It will need to take several short sleeps (cat-naps!) during the day in addition to a longer sleep at night.
Don't shut your kitten out at night; as yet it will not be able to fend for itself.

Feeding time

Do remember that a kitten's stomach is no bigger than a walnut, so it can eat only small portions.
Do feed it little and often—four meals a day should be sufficient.
Do vary the meals, but not the mealtimes. A suitable routine would be: warm milk, mushy cereal or milky porridge for breakfast; a little finely-minced meat towards midday; more warm milk at mid-afternoon; and

some mashed, carefully boned fish (perhaps mixed with a little warm milk) for supper.

Do remember that a kitten will take time to settle to new foods, depending on its age and taste.

Do reduce the number of meals and increase the size of them as the kitten grows. When fully grown, a cat may want no more than one good meal a day, but always have milk or water (whichever it prefers) available.

Do make couch-grass available to your kitten; this helps it to pass fur collected in the stomach after washing.

Don't make the mistake of trying to hurry your kitten on to tinned or dried foods. These should never form a cat's entire diet, anyway; cats are hunters at heart and love fresh, raw meat—the more often the better!

House-training your kitten

Do provide a dirt-tray for your kitten. You can buy either a metal or plastic one, or an old baking-tray, thoroughly cleaned, will do. Stand it on a newspaper (larger than the tray) and put a centimetre layer of cat-litter (obtainable from pet shops) or earth or sand in it—something the kitten can dig into.

Do take your kitten to the tray and place its front paws inside, moving them across in a scratching motion. Your kitten will soon learn what you are trying to teach it.

Do renew the cat-litter each time it becomes soiled.

Do wash the tray out often in order to keep it free from unwanted odours.

Don't lose your temper with your kitten if it soils the carpet; remember it is learning. Gently scold it and go through the scratching routine again.

Playing and grooming

Do play with your kitten, but never try to force it into a game.

Do keep a few 'toys' around. Kittens love playing 'tug-of-war' with a ball of wool or 'football' with a ping-pong ball.

Don't try to teach your kitten unnatural tricks.

Don't give up playing games as the kitten grows into a cat; 'kittens' of all ages love to play.

Do brush your kitten daily (twice each day if long-haired). This reduces the amount of fur the kitten will swallow when washing.

Don't brush against the fur; brush the way the fur grows.

Visiting the vet

Do make sure that by the time it is ten weeks old your kitten has paid a visit to the vet's or P.D.S.A.* surgery for an inoculation against Feline Infectious Enteritis, a serious, often fatal, disease. The inoculation will also help protect against Feline Distemper (cat 'flu).

Do watch for signs of sickness in your kitten. Coughing, sneezing, loss of appetite and high temperature should all receive attention from the vet.

Finally . . .

Do remember that a kitten is not like a puppy; it will not come at your beck and call. Cats are independent creatures; they like to do as their instincts tell them. But give a cat its freedom and it will reward you with many happy hours of companionship and fun.

Don't think this is everything you need to know about caring for a kitten. These are only the very basic DOs and DON'Ts—you'll find plenty more in books on the subject. *Do* read them—for your kitten's sake.

*People's Dispensary for Sick Animals